"It is my dream for us to be married."

Janos continued tenderly, "Tell me you'd like it, too, Sara."

"Yes, I would," she murmured dazedly. This handsome stranger from another world, with magic in his fingers, was actually asking her to marry him!

"You won't change your mind?" he demanded urgently, and she shook her head solemnly.

His arms encircled her. "Please forgive my impatience, Sara," he whispered. "It is becoming difficult for me to be in the same place as you without making love to you."

"I'll marry you as soon as possible, Janos, and together we'll make our dreams come true...."

Sara remembered it all as if it were yesterday. If only she'd known then how their brief bubble of romance would burst when it encountered sharp reality!

FLORA KIDD

passionate stranger

Harlequin Books

TORONTO • LONDON • LOS ANGELES • AMSTERDAM
SYDNEY • HAMBURG • PARIS • STOCKHOLM • ATHENS • TOKYO

Harlequin Presents edition published November 1981.
ISBN 0-373-10464-2

Original hardcover edition published in 1981
by Mills & Boon Limited

CHAPTER ONE

IT was an evening in May and in the purple-dark sky arching over the Los Padres mountains of California close to the Pacific Ocean, the stars hung like huge diamond pendants, their glitter reflected in the ever-moving water which surges towards the yellow sands and rugged rocks of one of the most spectacular coastlines in the world.

In the auditorium of a state university college, situated on five thousand acres of campus outside a pretty postcard-picturesque town famed for the old Spanish mission around which it had been built, the county symphony orchestra was holding its last concert of the season. Seated in the third row from the front of the middle section of chairs, Sara Cranston, who was over from England visiting her cousin Cecilia Merton, joined in the applause at the end of the lively overture.

The hand-clapping died down as the conductor left the stage. Several members of the orchestra followed him. Presumably they were not needed for the next item of music. After making sure that Cecilia, who played the flute, was still sitting in the woodwind section of the orchestra, Sara turned to the man who was on her left. He was Glenn Bixman, the brother-in-law of Myrna Bixman who was sitting on Sara's right. Myrna

was the President of the Symphony's Ladies'
Guild for the year and her husband, Charles
Bixman, who was sitting on her right, was one of
the orchestra's principal benefactors. He was also
both chairman and president of a local fruit and
vegetable canning company whose labels could be
found on most kitchen shelves throughout the
western hemisphere.

'What comes next?' Sara whispered to Glenn.

'Didn't you get a programme?' His square-
chinned, solid-looking face, which was tanned to
the usual Californian golden colour, expressed his
irritation at such an oversight. 'Here, take mine.'
He handed her the booklet of white paper, printed
in blue ink.

'You look very bored,' Sara said teasingly. Over
the past two weeks she had come to know Glenn
quite well, as he had been her escort on several
occasions. 'Don't you like classical music?'

'Not much.' He slanted a white smile at her,
his grey eyes softening between their bronze-
coloured lashes. 'I have to admit I'm only here
tonight because you are. I'm aiming to make the
most of the few days of your holiday here. I wish
you didn't have to go back to England. Isn't there
any way you could stay?'

'I don't know. I haven't thought about it,' she
replied evasively, opening the programme and
finding the right page. She read what was printed
in the second section of the first part of the programme. Brahms Violin Concerto in D, Opus 77.
Allegro non troppo; Addagio; Allegro giocoso ma

non troppo vivace. The name of the soloist was to be announced on the night of the concert on a sheet of paper to be included in the programme.

Sara flicked over another page. The loose sheet of paper slipped out and fluttered to the floor. Bending, she picked it up and turned it over. A photograph of the soloist took up about half the page and it seemed to leap out at her. She stared at it incredulously. Suddenly there was a strange roaring in her ears and she swayed where she sat. She looked round quickly, trying to shake off the feeling of faintness. The stage lights blurred before her eyes and for a few seconds the musicians and their instruments seemed to be suspended in mid-air, swinging from side to side. Breathing deeply, Sara fought for control.

It couldn't be true! She couldn't believe that Janos was the soloist at this concert. If it were true then surely Cecilia would have told her. For another thing, she doubted if he would come and play with a small orchestra like this one—a non-profit-making organisation formed and financially supported by local residents to encourage and promote the performance of orchestral music and which was hardly in a position to afford such a celebrity as Janos had become.

Almost reluctantly she looked down at the photograph again. It was a profile showing the slant of a high forehead under rebellious fronds of black hair, the proud curve of a slightly hooked nose and the determined jut of his chin. He was not smiling. He looked as she had often seen him look, withdrawn and melancholy, as if he were brooding on unhappy far-off incidents in his life; as if he were regretting the loss of someone he had loved dearly. The loose white shirt he was wearing, which was open almost to the waist, enhanced the dark romanticism of his appearance.

Clapping broke out again and she looked up. The conductor was returning. He was followed by the man in the photograph—Janos Vaszary. Formal clothes, black trousers, black tail coat, white tie, white ruffled shirt and white cummerbund fitted his tall figure to perfection and his longish black hair shimmered glossily under the lights. A violin tucked beneath his right arm, his bow in his hand, he moved to the front of the stage when the conductor gestured to him, introducing him to the audience. The clapping increased and he bowed gracefully from the hips. As he straightened up his brilliant glance flashed over the audience as if he were seeking for someone. Then he stepped back, put the violin beneath his chin and taking a note from the leader of the orchestra made sure his instrument was tuned correctly.

When that was done he looked up at the conductor, who was standing on the podium, and nodded. The conductor raised his hands. Both the orchestra and the audience became silent. It was a silence of excited anticipation. The conductor's right hand swept down. His left hand gestured to the cellists. Bows were lifted and were drawn in perfect unison across taut strings. Slowly, sonorously, sweetly yet sadly the first notes of the concerto were played.

Soon the reedlike sound of the oboe playing a different tune joined the cellos. The violins and other woodwind added their variations and sound swelled, filling the hall. Sara sat tensely, unable to take her eyes off the soloist as he waited for the time to come when he would assert himself and take over command of the musical argument.

If she had known that Janos was to be the soloist at this concert would she have come? She glanced uncertainly first at Glenn and then at Myrna Bixman. They were both staring at Janos too. Did they know, she wondered, that she was married to Janos? Had Cecilia told them? Certainly they would not connect her with him by name because ever since she had separated from him she had not used the name Vaszary.

But he was beginning to play with that sureness of attack and clarity of tone which had been produced by many hours of practice and much experience of performance. Assailed by the poignant sweetness and passion of the music, Sara closed her eyes and resting her head on her hand gave in to the torrent of memories which the music awoke, memories which she had tried so hard to obliterate from her mind over the past two years.

That high sweet melody he was playing now, so expressive of tender romantic feelings and yet so thoroughly masculine, was the first tune she had ever heard him play on the violin, and the whole of this movement, full of passionate vitality as it was, seemed to express the drama of their first meeting and their subsequent relationship, with its dark deep almost discordant undertones interwoven with the ear-piercing yet sensuous sound of the solo violin.

Over three years had passed since that first meeting, yet it was as vivid as if it had happened yesterday. Sara had been lying on her bed at the flat in Manchester, she remembered, talking on the phone to her Aunt Hilda about Cecilia's wedding which she was going to attend at the end of the week. She could even remember what she had been saying to her aunt when the front door bell had buzzed. She had been describing the dress she had intended to wear and the bell had been loud, insistent. She could almost hear it now. . . .

'Hang on a minute, Aunty,' she said into the mouthpiece. 'There's someone at the door. It's probably Brenda Marshall come to borrow something, as usual.'

'No, I won't hang on, love,' her aunt replied. 'We'll see you here tomorrow evening. About five?'

'I hope so. The forecast is for rain and some snow showers and that might slow me down.' The doorbell rang again. 'I must go now. 'Bye!'

'Drive carefully,' warned her aunt.

The receiver clattered down on the rest and Sara hurried through the small living room of the neat two-bedroom flat. Fully expecting to see Brenda, one of the teachers who lived in the flat next door, she flung open the door without hesitation, her lips slanting into a teasing smile, a derisive remark on the tip of her tongue. When she saw the shabbily-dressed, unshaven man who stood in the passage outside the door her smile faded quickly, she bit back the remark and quickly pushed the door forward until there was only a narrow space between its edge and the jamb.

'What do you want?' she demanded sharply. The hour was late and although she had heard recently that some people in the flats had been bothered by unwelcome callers she had not had anyone at her door before.

'I've come to see Cecilia,' he said, and there was a distinctly foreign lilt to the way he spoke English. 'Is she here?'

'No, she isn't.' She saw him frown in puzzlement and assumed that he had not understood the way she spoke. 'She is not here,' she repeated slowly and loudly, looking him over.

The dark suit he was wearing under an unbuttoned greyish-white trenchcoat was made of shoddy material and had definitely not been cut by an English tailor. He was not wearing a tie and his thin rather grubby-looking white shirt was open at the neck. At his feet was a battered leather suitcase and his shoes . . . well, his shoes were the worst she had ever seen being worn by anyone. She began to push the door closed, only to find that he had put a foot between the door and the jamb.

'This is the address she gave me,' he argued, and there was a touch of desperation in his manner which made her hesitate. 'This is flat four, number twelve Goodman Street and this is the city of Manchester?'

'Yes, but Cecilia doesn't live here any more. She's gone away,' Sara said firmly. 'I'm her cousin, Sara Cranston. Who are you?'

'Janos,' he replied briefly, staring at her with brilliant tawny eyes which were deep-set beneath straight black eyebrows. 'Didn't Cecilia tell you about me?'

'No—at least I don't think so. Where did you meet her?'

'In Austria, at Salzburg, the Mozart Festival last summer. She said that if I ever got to this country she would ...' He paused, frowned slightly, then continued, 'She said I should come to see her.' A faint smile curved his mouth, softening for a second the gauntness of his face. 'So here I am,' he added, spreading his hands out in a foreign gesture.

'I'm sorry she isn't here,' Sara said. She was still suspicious. With his shabby clothes and unshaven face he didn't seem to be the sort of person her fastidious young cousin would associate with. 'She's gone home.'

'Home?' he repeated, touching his forehead with long fingers. 'But isn't this her home?'

'I mean she's gone to her parents' house. They

live at Stonethwaite, up north. Oh, what's the matter?' He had gone a sickly grey colour and was actually swaying on his feet. 'Oh, please, you mustn't pass out!' she whispered frantically, and catching hold of his arm she draped it round her shoulders so that he wouldn't fall. 'You'd better come in and sit down for a while.'

Somehow she managed to guide him over to the settee, all the time wondering if he was pulling a trick just to get inside the flat. He sat down heavily on the settee and, leaning forward, put his head down on his knees, and she felt a certain relief. He was really faint. Hurrying back to the door, she pulled the suitcase inside. Closing the door, she went back to the settee and sat down beside him. She touched him on the shoulder, bracing herself to resist should he turn and attack her. But he didn't move. Elbows on his knees, head between his hands, he sat or rather sagged limply as if he had no more strength left.

'Can I get you something?' she asked.

'Food,' he muttered, his voice muffled by his hands. 'I haven't eaten today. Something to eat and drink, please.'

He spoke with a punctilious politeness which did much to dispel her fear that he might be a marauder.

'Of course, she said, and getting to her feet went into the kitchen.

What sort of food should she give to someone who hadn't eaten for a long time? Something gentle yet sustaining. She seemed to remember

Aunt Hilda giving her or Cecilia poached egg on toast after they had suffered from a stomach ailment, so she put a saucepan of water on the cooker to come to the boil and placed slices of bread in the toaster.

When she returned to the living room carrying a tray the man called Janos was leaning against the back of the settee with his eyes closed. He was still wearing his trenchcoat. Sara set the tray down on the coffee table and he opened his eyes.

'I am sorry,' he said slowly. 'Nothing like that has happened to me before.' He sat up, his glance going to the food on the tray.

'Please go ahead and eat,' Sara invited. 'But take it slowly.'

She picked up one of the big cushions she and Cecilia had made and which were scattered about the floor taking the place of chairs. Putting it down beside the coffee table, she sank down on it, her legs in their well-cut corduroy pants curving under her as she supported herself on one arm.

'Why haven't you eaten today?' she asked, her glance going to his hands as he manipulated the knife and fork. In contrast to the rest of his appearance they were scrupulously clean and the nails of the long well-shaped fingers were neatly trimmed.

He flashed her a sharp underbrowed glance and finished chewing the food that was in his mouth before replying.

'There was no time to stop for food,' he replied noncommittally. An elusively attractive smile quirked his lips. 'I am in a hurry to see Cecilia,' he added, his glance shifting over her curiously. 'I can see you are a relative of hers, but you are older, I think.'

'By three years. My mother and Cecilia's mother were sisters. I was only two when my mother died in an accident at the biscuit factory where she worked and Aunt Hilda and her husband, who are farmers, adopted me. I grew up thinking I was Cecilia's elder sister.'

'What happened to your father?' he asked.

'I don't know. He deserted my mother before I was born. I think he was a seaman.' There was a touch of defiance in her glance.

He made no comment but finished eating the food. Picking up the mug of milk she had brought for him, he drank, all the time staring at her curiously.

'Your hair is darker than Cecilia's,' he remarked as he set down the empty mug.

'Meaning mine is an ordinary dull brown while hers is a beautiful strawberry blonde,' she retorted dryly.

'No, not an ordinary brown. More like the coppery colour of beech leaves in autumn.'

'You speak very good English,' she said quickly, covering up her inward startled reaction to the compliment. No man had ever said anything like that to her before.

'I had a good teacher—my grandmother. She was English, a musician. She met my grandfather in Vienna when she was studying there. He was a violinist. I lived with them when I was a boy and she taught me to speak her language. She said I might need it one day,' he said quietly, and finished the milk.

'Are you an Austrian?' she asked.

'Hungarian,' he replied curtly, and set down the mug.

'Oh. But I thought . . .' She broke off, frowning. Hungary was a country behind the Iron Curtain, wasn't it? She had vague memories of its history; tales of a wild tempestuous people called Magyars who made music, of a struggle for freedom against various conquering invaders, and suddenly she remembered why it was she knew the name Janos. 'Hary Janos!' she exclaimed. 'He was a Hungarian folk hero and there's a piece of music about him by Kodaly. I heard it played at a concert I went to with Cecilia. Is Janos your last name, then?'

'First. In English it means John,' he said in that short way which she was beginning to realise meant he had no wish to give her more information about himself. 'The food was good, thank you,' he added.

'Can I get you anything else? More milk? I have some cake. Pound cake, we call it. It's quite filling.'

'I would like some, please,' he said, and pressed the back of his hand to his mouth to stifle a yawn.

It didn't take long for Sara to cut some slices of the pound cake and pour more milk, but when she returned to the living room, more questions on the tip of her tongue to ask her unexpected guest, she found he had taken off his trenchcoat and suit jacket and had stretched full length on the settee. With his head pillowed on one of the cushions he appeared to be asleep.

Sara set down the milk and cake. Her lips tightening in annoyance, she went over to the settee and touched his shoulder.

'Janos,' she said sharply, 'wake up! You can't sleep here. You must leave and go somewhere else to sleep.'

He didn't move and his eyelashes didn't quiver once. She bent over him, studying his face. The dark stubble of his beard which gave him such a scruffy appearance also drew attention to the sharpness of his high cheek-bones and the hollows about his eyes. Exhaustion was etched on his face quite clearly and he was so fast asleep that he was hardly breathing. Sympathy stirred in Sara, smothering for ever the suspicions she had felt. She couldn't make him wake up and leave. And what harm would it do to let him sleep there as long as he needed to sleep? None at all to her. Going into the bedroom which had been Cecilia's until a few days ago, she picked up the down-filled duvet and carrying it into the living room laid it over the sleeping man. Taking the tray, she switched off the ceiling light, leaving the desk lamp on only, and went into the kitchenette.

Why had Cecilia never told her about Janos? As she washed the few dishes Sara thought back to the end of the previous summer and Cecilia's return from her tour of Europe with the student orchestra in which she had been the leading flute-player. Cecilia had talked of many people and many places. Had she much to say about Salzburg? Not really, except to say it had been a wonderful experience and that she would never forget the city with the fortress on one hill and the monastery on the other, its maze of medieval streets where Mozart had once walked. She had never mentioned a young man called Janos. She had been much too excited about another young man she had met in Paris, Philip Merton, a wealthy sophisticated American from California who had followed her when she had returned to Manchester and had lost no time in proposing marriage to her.

Leaving the kitchenette, Sara went through to her bedroom and closed the door. For a few moments she hesitated, looking down at the phone. It would be best if she checked up on Janos. She picked up the receiver and in a few minutes she was talking to her aunt again.

'Sorry to be ringing so late, Aunty, but is Cecilia home now?'

'Yes, she's just come in.'

'I'd like to speak to her, please.'

'She's here, now, Sara. Hang on a sec.'

There was a clattering sound as the receiver was put down at the other end of the line. It was picked up again and Cecilia's soft, slightly breathless voice said,

'Hello, Sara. What's happened?'

'A man called Janos is here.'

'Janos?' Surprise lilted through Cecilia's voice. 'Janos who?'

'I don't know his last name. He didn't tell me. He said he met you last summer in Salzburg.'

'Oh, that Janos. Oh, my God!' Cecilia was more than surprised by now. 'I didn't believe he meant what he said. I didn't believe he would come,' she babbled.

'Well, he has come, and now he's asleep on the settee and I can't wake him up,' replied Sara sharply. It wasn't the first time she had become irritated with her cousin's vagueness. 'Cecilia, who is he?'

'A violinist. He played in an ensemble from Hungary at the Festival. He's a very fine musician and I went out with him a few times.' Cecilia broke off and Sara could hear her breath quivering agitatedly over the line. 'When he had to go back to Hungary I told him that if he ever came to England I'd ... but I never believed he would come. I was told that he was in trouble with the Hungarian authorities for trying to defect to the West and that he might be put in prison when he returned to Budapest. Sara, you haven't told him where I am, have you?'

'Yes, I have, but so far he isn't any the wiser. I don't think he knows where Stonethwaite is.'

'Have you told him why I'm here? Have you told him I'm getting married tomorrow?'

'No, not yet. Should I?'

'I ... oh, I don't know. Perhaps it would be

best not to. You mustn't let him come here, though.' Cecilia sounded really panicky. 'You must stop him from coming here somehow, at least until after the wedding is over and Philip and I have gone away.'

'But how can I stop him? And why should I? Why don't you want him to come and see you? What did you and he do together in Salzburg?' Sara demanded. 'Were you lovers? Is that why you don't want him turning up at your wedding?'

'No, oh no, there was nothing like that. Please don't ask any more questions. I can't answer them with everyone here sitting around and listening in. Just do as I ask, please, Sara. Stop him from coming here until after I've gone. I don't care what you do, just stop him from coming.'

'Oh, all right. I'll do what I can.'

'Thanks a million! I knew I could depend on you.'

With a sigh Sara replaced the receiver. It wasn't the first time in her life Cecilia had passed on a responsibility to her or had depended on her to help her out of some tangle. Oh well, there was nothing she could do about it tonight, she thought as she began to undress. Maybe tomorrow morning would bring a solution to the problem. Maybe Janos would leave before she woke up.

But her unwelcome guest was still fast asleep on the settee when she went into the living room next morning. Going over to the settee, she looked down at him.

'Janos—wake up!' She spoke harshly. He didn't

move, so she put a hand on his shoulder, feeling the warmth of his skin through the thin cotton, and shook him. 'Janos, wake up!' she repeated.

His thick black lashes spread like tiny fans on his cheeks, giving him a curiously vulnerable appearance. They quivered, his eyelids lifted and his tawny-gold eyes, hazed with sleep, looked directly at her. He stared uncomprehendingly at her for a few seconds.

'Come on,' she urged, 'get up. I have to go to work in an hour's time. I promised I'd look in at the mill on my way to Stonethwaite, and I'd like you to be gone from here before I leave. You can have a bath, if you like. You look as if you need one.'

Slowly he pushed up on one elbow, raising his other hand to rake fingers through his longish tousled black hair. His shirt had become un-buttoned and Sara could see the white bones of his ribs gleaming through the hair-darkened skin. He looked round the room, then looked at her again.

'Have I been here all night?' he asked.

'Yes.' She put on her sternest expression. 'I couldn't wake you up last night.'

'I apologise. I meant only to sleep for a few minutes.' His polite apology, the softening of the severe line of his lips by the smile which lit up the sombreness of his face, did much to change her attitude.

'Well, you've slept for a good eight hours,' she said. 'I'm going to cook some breakfast now. It should be ready by the time you've bathed. The bathroom is over there. You'll find clean towels in the cupboard.'

'Thank you.'

In the kitchenette Sara set the small table and put bacon in the frying pan, wondering what she would tell Janos when he asked to see Cecilia again. She could tell him it was impossible because Cecilia was getting married tomorrow. No—she shook her head—it would be best not to mention Cecilia's wedding. It would be best to say Cecilia had already left the country. No, she couldn't say that either, because she had already told him that her cousin was at Stonethwaite.

In a way she could understand why her cousin didn't want him turning up at Stonethwaite. Shabbily dressed, half starved, he wouldn't fit in with the rest of the guests. He would be most unwelcome. Sara laughed to herself rather mockingly as she imagined how Philip Merton's wealthy relatives and friends would look down their noses at Janos whose shoes were beyond repair.

Yet when he appeared in the kitchenette he didn't look scruffy any more, even though he was still wearing the same shirt of greyish-white coarse cotton and the same badly-cut trousers. Wide-shouldered and slim-hipped, he wore his shabby clothes with a certain elegance and although pale, without beard stubble his face appeared clean-angled, the cheeks too hollow, it was true, but the nose finely moulded, the mouth long-lipped and firmly set. It was an intelligent face, yet it was tough too, as if the bones were fashioned from tempered steel. His hair, now clean and shining damply, glinted with gold and blue lights as it slid forward in an attractive wave across his forehead.

'Please sit down,' said Sara, waving a hand towards the table. 'I'm afraid it's egg again, fried this time with bacon. An English breakfast.' She placed a plate of food in front of him. 'There's tea too, and toast and marmalade.' She sat down opposite to him.

'It was kind of you to let me sleep here,' he said.

'There wasn't much I could do to stop you,' she said with a touch of humour. 'You went out like a light while I was getting the cake. You must have been very tired. Did you come straight here from Hungary?'

'No.' The curt answer was deliberately off-putting and he didn't look at her.

'Have you come here on business?'

'I have come to see Cecilia,' he replied stubbornly.

'But coming to see her can't be the only reason for your coming to this country,' she objected.

'It was one reason I gave to the refugee organisation in Vienna when I applied for permission to enter this country. It was accepted,' he said coolly. 'Where is this Stonethwaite you talk about, where Cecilia is now?'

'In the Lakes.' If he could be uncommunicative

so could she. The answer was vague. He wouldn't
know where the Lakes were.

'How would I get to Stonethwaite?' he asked,
and she sensed that stubbornness in him again.

'It isn't an easy journey,' she parried, stalling
for time while she thought quickly of ways to stop
him from going.

'It couldn't be any more difficult than the journey I made from Budapest to Vienna last year,'
he said dryly. 'I had to swim a river at dead of
night. Then I walked, again mostly at night.'

'Then you are a defector!' Sara exclaimed, her
eyes widening.

'I am a refugee,' he corrected her, his mouth
twisting.

'Did you leave for political reasons?' she asked.

'I left because there was no longer any reason
for me to stay,' he replied evasively. 'Can I go to
Stonethwaite directly from here? Is there a train
or a bus? I don't have very much English money.'

'You would have to take a train,' she told him.

'Does it go straight to Stonethwaite?' he persisted.

'No. Stonethwaite is a village. You'd have to
take the train or a long-distance bus, which is
cheaper, to the nearest city,' she replied slowly,
being as vague as she could.

'And that is?' he rapped, and she looked up.

Eyes as cold and as blank as an eagle's met hers
across the table and she knew with a strange shiver
of excitement that he wasn't going to be put off.
Steely determination to overcome any obstacle in

his way was expressed in his face. It had carved
the jut of his jaw, moulded the set of his mouth.

'Carlisle,' she said. 'From there you'd have to
take another bus.'

'So what time are you leaving to catch the train
or the long-distance bus?' he asked, almost
casually.

'Me?' Her surprise was genuine.

'Yes, you. When you were waking me up you
said that you are going to Stonethwaite today,
after you have been to your work.'

'Oh, yes, I did, didn't I?' she admitted, annoyed
with herself for being so careless. 'But I'm not
going by train or bus. I'm driving.'

It took him a few seconds to absorb and understand what she had said but during that time he
didn't look away from her once. Still cold and
blank, his gaze remained fixed on her face.

'What will you be driving?' he asked at last.

'My car?'

'You own a car?' His eyes widened slightly.
'Then you must have a very good job and earn
much money.'

'It's not a bad job . . . but please don't get the
wrong idea about what I earn. I make a comfortable living if I'm not extravagant. As for the car,'
she laughed a little, 'it isn't a limousine by any
stretch of the imagination. It's a Mini and I
bought it secondhand.'

'What is your work?'

'I work for a textile company as a designer.'
She saw him look puzzled and explained further.

'I studied graphic design at a polytechnic college and now I design the patterns for furnishing fabrics which are made from cotton. We use a silk screen process for printing the patterns on the cloth. They're quite expensive to buy.' She glanced at her watch. 'Heavens, I must fly if I don't want to be late. It's twenty to nine already. Are you sure you've had enough to eat?'

Janos pushed back his chair and stood up.

'Yes, thank you. Excuse me,' he said with that careful politeness. 'I will go and get ready to leave.'

He went into the living room. Collecting up the dirty dishes, Sara piled them in the sink and ran water on them. Then she rushed into her bedroom, flung on the jacket of her tweed suit, grabbed her sheepskin jacket and the suitcase she had packed the night before and hurried into the living room, to be greeted by a trill of notes played on the violin.

Janos was standing in the middle of the room, a violin tucked under his chin, and was playing very softly a sweet melody on extremely high notes. Amazed by the tender quality of the sound and the perfection of his playing, Sara could only stand and stare at him until with a series of triumphant chords he brought the melody to an end. Dropping her case and jacket, she clapped her hands in enthusiastic and spontaneous applause, and he spun round to face her.

'That was beautiful!' she exclaimed, surprised at her own reaction to his playing. Normally very

reserved, she wasn't given to showing her feelings
so naturally. 'What were you playing?'

'It was the end of the first movement of the
Brahms Violin Concerto. You liked it, hmm? It is
one of my favourites too. Perhaps you would like
the second movement, too. It is very romantic.'

Lifting his bow, he played another haunting
melody and came towards her, his eyes, now a
dark tawny colour, looking right into hers, and
she stood there as if transfixed, trapped in time
and space by the lovely sound he could produce
from four strings stretched over an elegantly
shaped box of wood; feeling as if she were being
serenaded by a lover who was trying to coax her
to submit to his lovemaking and to reach with
him the heights of joy and the depths of passion.

'No, oh, no,' she whispered rather wildly,
breaking the spell abruptly. 'I'll be late for work.'

He stopped playing at once, dragging his bow
across the strings in a discordant ugly sound.

'You did not like that?' he asked.

'I liked it very much, but I can't stay any longer
listening to you play,' Sara told him practically.
'I must go to work and you must leave this flat.
What are you going to do? Where will you go
now?' she added, suddenly concerned about him,
remembering he was a stranger in a·strange land.

'To the station to find out when I can catch a
train or a bus to Carlisle,' he said, going over to
the violin case lined with red velvet, which he had
left lying open on the settee, and laying the violin
in it. 'Do you think I'll be able to get to

Stonethwaite today?' he asked as he closed the case and put it in the suitcase which contained a pathetically few clothes.

'How did you swim the river with your violin?' Sara asked curiously, not wanting to answer his question, knowing that he could get to Stonethwaite that day if he went to the station now.

'I didn't,' he said, slipping on his jacket. 'When I went back to Hungary from Austria last summer I left it with a friend and when I returned to Vienna at Christmas, it was there waiting for me to collect it. I have carried it in the suitcase so that I do not have two pieces of luggage to take care of.' He picked up his trenchcoat and slung it loosely about his shoulders like a cloak. 'You did not answer my question,' he went on. 'Will I be able to get to Stonethwaite and see Cecilia today?'

'Why is it so important for you to see Cecilia?' she asked.

'Why don't you want me to see her?' he countered, his eyes flashing angrily as he showed he had noticed she was evading his question. He picked up his suitcase and walked to the door. 'Thank you very much for letting me stay the night here and for giving me food,' he said, stiffly polite again. 'I shall not forget your kindness. I go now to the station. We shall meet again at Stonethwaite, perhaps.'

'Wait, wait!' Sara managed to put herself between him and the door. Leaning back against its panels, she gazed up at him, realising that this

was one time in her life she would have to use
those feminine wiles which she had often derided
and looked down upon. Tipping back her head,
unaware of the beauty of her long white-skinned
throat arched back against the autumnal coppery
blaze of her thick shoulder-length hair, she smiled
up at him warmly. 'It isn't that I don't want you
to see Cecilia,' she explained. 'It's just that . . .
well, it's an awkward journey and it seems silly
for you to travel by public transport when I'm
driving to Stonethwaite this afternoon. If . . . if
you'd like to wait here until twelve o'clock, until
I've finished the work I have to do this morning,
I'll come back for you and you can come with me
in the car. It's quite a long drive and I like to
have company. I'm always worried in case one of
the tires punctures—I'm not very good at changing wheels. Would you like to do that, wait for
me here, and then we'll go together?'

He was staring at her, not suspiciously, nor
speculatively, but as if he were momentarily
dazzled, and she realised how close they were to
each other. Awareness of him on the physical
level, of the brilliance of his black-rimmed tawny-
gold eyes gazing at her in wonderment, of the fine
bone structure of his face, of the gypsy-darkness
of his hair and golden-brownness of his skin,
washed over her like a sea-wave and caused her
skin to tingle and her breath to catch in her throat.
She felt threatened by him but could not move
away from him. Nor did she understand why she
should feel that way.

'Your eyes are green,' he said softly and quite inconsequently, 'clear and cool as the sea until you smile. Then they sparkle with sunshine. You should smile more often. You are very pretty when you do. So pretty I would like to . . .' His parted lips were only an inch or two away from hers when his teeth snapped together sharply and he stepped back from her. Raking his free hand through his hair, he glanced away from her, frowning, his profile withdrawn and fierce, eagle-like. 'It might not be safe for me to travel with you,' he muttered.

'But I'm a good driver,' she protested, deliberately misunderstanding him, trying to pretend his recent remarks about her eyes and smile, the way he had looked at her hungrily as well as admiringly, made her feel even more threatened. 'Will you wait here for me to come back for you?'

He turned his head slowly to look at her, suspicion clearly expressed in his face.

'No,' he said curtly, 'I will not wait here for you. I will go to the station and travel by train.'

'But it would be more sensible, more direct for you to go with me. It would save you money and you'd be sure of getting there today,' she argued. She was finding it difficult to be deceitful. Naturally honest and straightforward in her dealing with other people, she had never practised seduction in any form.

'Would I?' His eyebrows slanted mockingly. 'Perhaps.'

'Of course you would,' she retorted, suddenly

annoyed with him for doubting her.

'But how can I be sure you will come back here for me?' he argued back. 'You might forget and by the time I realise you are not coming back for me it will be too late for me to catch a train to Carlisle and get to Stonethwaite today.'

'You're not very trusting, are you?' she protested.

'I have reason not to trust anyone. Many times I have been betrayed by people I have trusted. Now I trust only myself. So will you let me pass, please, and I will go to the station.'

'I ... er ... oh, you're really very proud and difficult to deal with,' Sara exclaimed. 'And I haven't any more time to spend arguing with you.'

'Then don't,' he retorted coolly. 'Just open the door and let me go.'

'I can't,' she said unthinkingly, and seeing his eyebrows go up in haughty surprise she added quickly, 'I mean, I can't let you travel to Stonethwaite by train when I'm going there myself by car. Cecilia will be very cross with me if I do, so I'll take you to work with me now and you can wait for me there. I don't suppose anyone will complain.' She noticed him stiffen proudly. 'Oh, please don't look like that—I didn't mean to offend you. Please come with me, Janos.' This time her smile was sincere. 'I would really like to have your company on the drive to Stonethwaite.'

'I was hoping you might say that,' he drawled, a slight smile softening the set of his mouth and glinting in his eyes. 'Thank you, Sara. I'll be pleased to come with you.'

'And you won't mind waiting for me at the mill?'

'I am very good at waiting when it is for something I want very much,' he replied enigmatically.

CHAPTER TWO

THE first movement of the concerto came to its surprisingly rushed and cheerful ending. There was a moment of silence and then applause burst out in sheer spontaneous appreciation of the soloist's performance, people clapping and shouting when they should not have been clapping and shouting, between movements. The conductor turned round, his pink perspiring face showing his displeasure at the unconventional, uninhibited behaviour of the audience. But Janos didn't look displeased. He was smiling and acknowledging with a bow the applause which he knew he deserved and which he had always said would be his once he had established himself as a soloist.

Startled by the noise of clapping out of her memories of her first meeting with him, Sara opened her eyes and looked at him, and it seemed to her that as he wiped his brow with a large white handkerchief he looked right back at her. But surely he couldn't see her? Her face would be just a pale blur to him, one of many beyond the glare of footlights. Yet he didn't look away from her as he tucked the handkerchief in his trouser pocket.

The conductor rapped sharply on the rail of his podium to call the audience to order and after some more shufflings and whisperings everyone went quiet. The conductor raised his hands again

as the musicians watched him. His right hand
floated down in a graceful movement and with a
slow melody played on the oboe the second
movement began.

A sigh shook through Sara and she closed her
eyes again, unable to look any more at Janos while
he waited for his turn to play. Regret was surging
through her at the sound of the romantic tune;
regret for the loving relationship she had thought
existed between her and Janos; a relationship
which had been ripped apart and destroyed by a
few hasty, jealous words uttered in anger.

The weaving of the relationship had begun, although she had not realised it at the time, that
morning when she had invited him to accompany
her on the drive to Stonethwaite. At the mill,
while she had supervised the silk screening of her
new design for curtain material, her mind had
been busy with plans for slowing down the drive
north. Secretly she had hoped that the heavy
squalls of icy sleet which were hitting the city
would turn to snow once she was among the
fells of north Lancashire and Cumbria.

At twelve o'clock the print of the design was
made and she went through to the office of Tom
Caldwell, the manager of the design department
of Ferris Furnishing Fabrics Ltd. Janos was
there, leafing through a magazine which someone
had given him, and he rose to his feet politely
when she entered so that Tom, who would not
have normally stood up, was forced to get to his
feet too.

'All finished?' asked Tom, coming round his desk towards her.

'Yes. It looks fine,' Sara turned to Janos. 'I hope you haven't been bored while you've been waiting?' She was quite relieved to find him still there. Once or twice she had wondered if he had left and gone to the station.

'No.' He smiled at her and his tawny eyes held a disturbingly warm glint of admiration. 'Mr Caldwell has entertained me very well. I have been on a tour of the mill and seen the various ways in which cotton can be woven. I have been shown some of the latest designs for curtain materials and have learned that Sara Cranston is a name which is becoming associated with all that is best in contemporary design.'

To her own surprise Sara felt the blood rush into her cheeks. Usually she was able to take admiration of her ability to design exciting new patterns in her stride and accept it as something which she knew she deserved.

'Oh, you mustn't take any notice of what Tom says about me,' she replied, trying to laugh off the sudden surge of pleasure she felt because this stanger whom she was about to trick was looking at her with respect as well as admiration. 'He's biased because much of what I know about good design I've learned from him.' She turned to Tom. 'We're leaving now. I'll be back on Monday afternoon, all being well.'

'The weather forecast isn't good for the Lake District,' he said, frowning at her. 'It would be safer to go by train.'

'We wouldn't get one until this evening,' she replied coolly, pulling on her sheepskin jacket.

'You'll keep to the motorway, then,' said Tom. 'That's sure to get priority for snow clearance.'

'Yes,' she replied serenely.

'And ring me, at home, when you get there,' he persisted, standing between her and Janos. 'I'll be worried about you,' he added, his brown eyes holding hers. 'Sara, do you have to go?'

'Of course I do. I promised Cecilia I'd be at her wedding. Don't look so anxious, Tom. I've driven to Stonethwaite lots of times without any trouble. And I'm not going to ring you—Anne wouldn't like it if I did,' she added softly. Anne was his wife.

'I'd feel better if you were going alone,' he murmured, glancing out of the corner of his eyes in Janos's direction and jerking his head towards him. 'Do you have to take him with you?' He mouthed the words so that Janos wouldn't hear.

'It's all right, Tom. I know what I'm doing,' she whispered. 'He's a friend of Cecilia's.'

'All right.' He sighed heavily. 'But be careful.'

'I will.' Sara looked past him at Janos, who had turned away from them politely and was looking out of a window at a view of brick walls and chimneys. 'Ready, Janos? We'll stop for something to eat on the way.'

She didn't take the route which would have led her to the motorway that sweeps up across the

Midlands of England from the London area to the border town of Carlisle. In fact she managed to get entangled in a maze of traffic in the middle of Manchester, and by the time she had escaped from it and was on the road to Preston intending to make a more devious route to Stonethwaite, it was after one o'clock and the sleet was turning to snow. Halfway between Manchester and Preston she stopped at a restaurant where she knew the service would be slow and they would be delayed even longer.

'Does it usually snow here at this time of the year?' Janos asked as they waited for the food they had ordered to be brought to them.

'Not usually, but sometimes March is colder in one year than in another. And the snow may not last. By tomorrow it could all be gone. Weather is very changeable in this country.'

'Changeable, like a woman,' he remarked with a slight taunting smile as he looked away from the window past which big white flakes were whirling and straight at her.

'I can't agree. Not all women are changeable. Once I've made up my mind about something or someone, I rarely change it.'

'Have you made up your mind about Mr Caldwell?' he asked.

'What do you mean? Why should I make up my mind about Tom?' asked Sara.

'I could be wrong,' he murmured, 'but I have the impression he likes you very much and would like to be your lover.'

'Tom? My lover?' she exclaimed. 'Oh, no!' She burst out laughing and shook her head from side to side so that her hair belled out about her face. 'He isn't that sort of person. He's married. He and I are friends, that's all, as well as being colleagues at work. We're not lovers, nor are we likely to be.'

The yellow-flecked tawny eyes watching her narrowed a little, but their gaze didn't falter.

'Yet I have a feeling he was warning me off his property,' he said quietly. 'He did not like for me to travel with you in this way. He does not want you to be alone with a suspicious-looking foreigner.'

'Did he say so to you?' she asked sharply, remembering how Tom had said he would feel better if she were travelling alone.

'He asked me many questions, like a policeman, about how I came here and why I wanted to see Cecilia,' Janos replied tautly, obviously annoyed.

'And I suppose you answered in the same way that you answered me last night and this morning, yet you're surprised he's suspicious of you,' she remarked. 'You know, Janos, you're only getting what you deserve. How can you expect me or Tom or anyone else to trust you when you won't trust anyone with information about yourself?' she argued. 'For example, you haven't told me your last name yet.'

'It is Vaszary. And I had thought this was a free country where people did not ask questions,' he retorted with a flash of anger. 'But we are talking about different things. Mr Caldwell does not trust me not because I refused to tell him anything about myself, but because I am going to be alone with you for a few hours and because I am a man. He is jealous because he believes you're his property.'

'I resent being referred to as someone's property,' she protested hotly. 'I don't belong to anyone. I belong to myself.' She gave him a direct challenging glance. 'If you're going to stay in this part of the world you'd better get rid of any old-fashioned notions you have about women being the property of men.'

'It isn't I who has the old-fashioned notions,' he replied, 'it is Mr Caldwell. He likes you better than his wife. He worries about you and wants to protect you and behaves as if he has the right to do so. Are you not aware of this?'

It was his turn to challenge her, and she was saved from having to reply because the waitress came with their food, two plates of shepherd's pie and the accompanying vegetables. As they began to eat Sara glanced surreptitiously at Janos across the table. He was very astute, she thought, and noticed far too much. She was aware of Tom's feelings for her and had for some time been trying to ignore him, knowing instinctively that once she showed an interest in him or any sign of returning his affection he would leave Anne. And she didn't want to be involved in anything like that. She didn't wish to be the cause of the break-up of anyone's marriage.

'Yes, I am aware of how Tom feels,' she said at last, speaking lightly. 'But he's married to Anne and as far as I'm concerned that makes any relationship between him and myself a no-no.'

'So you are not in love with him?'

'Heavens, no!' She laughed again and Janos looked up at her, the expression in his eyes matching the laughter in hers as he smiled again. 'I'm not in love with anyone, not yet. Do you mind if we talk about something else?'

'Because you are afraid?' he asked.

'Afraid?' she repeated in puzzlement. 'Of what?'

'Of love, or of falling in love. Is that why you do not want to discuss it?'

'No, it isn't,' she retorted. 'I don't want to discuss my personal affairs with you, that's all.'

'Because I am a suspicious foreigner?' he asked tauntingly.

'No. Because they're none of your business,' she countered sharply.

He gave her a glinting, mocking glance and they ate the rest of the meal in silence.

By the time they left the restaurant it was past two o'clock and the sky was a thick leaden grey from which the snowflakes whirled down steadily. But most of the flakes seemed to be melting as they touched the ground and the road was quite clear, although its surface was wet and greasy.

'Is there any way I can help?' Janos asked as the little car sped northwards between fields streaked with white. 'I would offer to drive, but I do not have a licence for this country and I do not know the way. Perhaps there is a map I could look at so I could navigate for you. The visibility is not very good.'

'There isn't a map,' Sara said sharply. She didn't want him to look at the map and find out there was a more direct way to Stonethwaite than the way she had chosen. 'I don't need one. I know the way very well because I've driven to Stonethwaite many times. It's really quite straightforward. We go along this road to Lancaster and from there to Kendal. When we reach that town we'll take a road to the left to-wards Windermere and from there we'll go over the Kirkstone Pass to Ullswater.'

'Then we are not going along the road which Mr Caldwell suggested.'

'No. This is a much more direct way,' she re-plied coolly, hoping she would be forgiven for lying.

It was a way on which they were much more likely to be delayed by the weather too, she thought hopefully. Already the road was becom-ing slippery with slushy snow and, as they went higher into the fells on narrower, more twisted roads, the chances of them reaching Stonethwaite that night or even next morning would become more and more remote and they would have to stop somewhere, possibly at the inn on the Kirkstone pass, if they ever got there. Or perhaps in Windermere before even attempting the pass. But wherever she chose to stop Janos would have to accept her decision not to go any farther that night because he wouldn't know there was any alternative.

As she drove along the qualms she had had about deceiving him faded from her mind. Nor was she worried any more about not arriving in time for Cecilia's wedding. In fact she felt strangely lighthearted and reckless, most unusual for her, as if she were setting out on an adventure; an adventure in the snow with a suspicious-looking foreigner.

She grinned to herself and glanced sideways at Janos. He had slumped down in the seat to rest his head against the support at the back and had closed his eyes. Was he sleeping? She hoped so, because then he wouldn't become suspicious of what she was doing.

After Lancaster the snowflakes came down faster and much more thickly. Darkness set in. Staring ahead of her through the windscreen, Sara found the repetitive pattern made by the flakes whirling towards the car mesmerising. Seeing beyond them was difficult and she had to drive quite slowly as she approached Kendal.

'How far now?' Janos spoke quietly beside her.

'Oh, miles and miles yet,' she replied airily, hoping she wouldn't miss the road off to the left which would take them to Windermere. 'Do you think you could watch for a sign by the side of the road? It will have the name Windermere on it.'

'Could you spell the name?' he asked. 'I cannot tell from the way you say it what it will look like.'

She did as he asked and slowed down even more because she could feel the wheels sliding on the untouched snow which was piling up on the road, and she wondered ruefully if she would have to stop before she reached Windermere.

'I can see a sign,' said Janos suddenly. 'Slow down so I can read what it says.'

Sara put her foot cautiously on the brake and changed down to second gear. The little car slid sideways, out into the middle of the road.

'Now we are past the sign, but I can see the other road,' said Janos. 'Turn to the left if you can.'

She turned the wheels left and the car slithered into the narrow secondary road. For a moment she thought it was going to continue to slip right off the road into the ditch at the side, then the tires bit into the smooth snow and she was able to drive forward.

The road was much narrower and more twisted than she had remembered it, and after driving for a while she began to wonder if she had taken the right turning.

'Are you sure the name on the sign was Windermere?' she asked.

'No, I am not sure. We were past it before I could read it,' Janos replied. 'What is the matter? Are we on the wrong road?'

'I . . . I . . . think we must be,' she muttered, pulling on the steering wheel, trying to keep the car from slipping and straining her eyes to see beyond the snowflakes that swirled ceaselessly towards the windscreen in a V formation. 'There are many more bends in it than I remember . . . oh, dear, I don't think we're going to make it round this one!'

In spite of her efforts to control it the car slid right across the road and hit a telephone post. Sara was jerked forward, her forehead banged against the windscreen and everything went black.

She became aware of a dull ache at the front of her head and of something extremely cold touching her face, ice-cold and wet. Someone was rubbing snow across her forehead. She opened her eyes and saw snowflakes falling beyond the window of the car.

'What happened?' she asked.

'The car hit a post and you banged your head.' The voice with its foreign accent came from close above her. She moved her head and found it was resting against his shoulder. He had one arm around her. 'How do you feel?' he asked. 'Nothing is broken, I hope?'

'No, I don't think so. It's just my head that hurts.' She touched her forehead and found a bump swelling. 'Are you all right?'

'Bumped my head also, but not as hard as you did.' His arms tightened about her as she tried to move away from him. 'Are you sure you want to move? Wouldn't it be best if you rested a little?' he asked softly.

Sara relaxed against him again, glad of his arm about her glad of the comfort offered by his hard shoulder.

'I'm sorry,' she muttered. 'I didn't mean this to happen. I thought we might have to stop somewhere on the way, but not like this, not miles from anywhere. We're really stuck now. We'll never get to Stonethwaite tonight.'

'When you feel you can move we'll go and look for some habitation,' he murmured, and she felt the movement of his jaw against the top of her head. 'Do you think there are any houses along this road?'

'If it's the road I think it is there's a small village farther along with an old coaching inn where we might be able to stay for the night. If it isn't open we could ask one of the villagers to help us. I'm sure somebody will when they know we've had an accident. Unless we can push the car back on to the road.'

'I do not think we can,' he said. 'I have looked and it is tilted into a bank of snow.' He was quiet for a moment, then he asked, 'Does it make you anxious not being able to get to Stonethwaite tonight?'

'No. Although Cecilia's parents might worry if I don't arrive. I'll have to try and phone them,' she told him. It was pleasant lying against him in the dark and in spite of the cold which was seeping into the car she was reluctant to move. 'Does it worry you?'

'No. I think I am glad that this has happened and that we are not going to reach Stonethwaite,' Janos replied softly.

She lifted her head and tried to see his face, but all she could see was the shape of his head, dark against the snow-light coming in through the window behind him.

'Why are you glad?' she whispered, aware

suddenly of unspoken messages passing between
them on a wavelength which was beyond the control of either of them.

'Because I will spend another night with you,'
he whispered, and his fingers touched her cheek
in a gently seductive caress.

The normal Sara, the one who hadn't been
recently hit on the head would have pulled away
with a sharp remark, probably telling him not to
be silly. She would have started to get out of the
car and would have organised the next move, to
find somewhere to stay for the night. But at the
moment she seemed to lack any desire to change
her position because she liked the feel of his fingers against her skin as they slid down and along
her jaw, round to the nape of her neck. She liked
too what was happening inside her in reaction to
his touch, the sudden flare-up of excitement
making her heart beat faster and the blood boil in
her veins.

She reached out and touched his face, the tips
of her fingers expressing her wish to know more
about him, pressing over the hard boss of his
cheekbone, slithering down to linger temptingly
on the curve of his lips. His breath escaped in a
little hiss, his fingers stroked her neck. Her head
tipped back, her lips parted. When his lips cool
yet tender touched hers she closed her eyes and
lifting her arms put them round him to hold him
closely.

Her response unleashed the control he had been
keeping over his desires and his mouth opened

hungrily to feed on the sweet softness and moistness of hers. Her senses reeled under that erotic demand. Passion exploded between them, blasting away suspicion and caution, its heat moulding them together for a short while there in the icy refrigerator of the little box-like car.

But soon neither of them could ignore the cold which was attacking their extremities and in spite of the desire that was boiling within him Janos began to shiver, his poor clothing and broken shoes no protection against the low temperature. Still holding him, Sara moved her mouth from beneath his and spoke against the roughness of his jaw.

'We can't stay the night here—we'll freeze if we do. We must move. We'll walk to the village ... that is if you can in those shoes.'

'I have walked a long way in these same shoes,' he whispered, still holding her. 'But wherever we go, we'll still spend the night together, hmmm?'

'You mean, in the same room?' she asked, suddenly wary and trying to push away from him.

'Yes.'

'I ... I ... don't know. I'm not sure. I haven't known you very long. In fact, I don't know you at all,' she said quickly, trying to assert her usual cool poise. It wasn't the first time a man had wanted to sleep with her, but she had always been able to deal with the situation before, pleasantly yet firmly making it clear that she was not available. But this was different. Janos was different. 'Just because I let you ... just because we

kissed . . .' She broke off, searching for a way to
tell him without hurting his feelings too much.
'What I'm trying to say is . . . that a kiss between
us doesn't mean I'm willing to . . . to go to bed
with you,' she finished rather lamely.

'You do not like me,' he accused. 'Then why
did you return my kiss?'

'I . . . oh, I don't know,' she retorted. 'Why did
you kiss me?'

'Because I like you. Because I wanted to show
you I am glad you are not hurt too badly. My
emotions run strongly and I have to show them.'
He paused. 'I think that perhaps it is not the same
with you,' he went on in a low voice. 'You keep
your feelings in a deep-freeze condition. You are
inhibited.'

'I'm not!' she objected, and then shivered vio-
lently. 'Oh, I'm not sitting here any longer. It's
too cold.'

'You are right,' he said with a laugh. 'It is too
cold here to make love satisfactorily.'

It wasn't easy to get out of the tilted-over car
and once she was out Sara was glad of her warmly
lined high boots because she found herself standing in calf-deep snow. She managed to open the
boot and they took out their cases. Leading the
way, she struggled through the drift up to the
road.

Snow had stopped falling and clouds had
cleared from the sky. Above stars glittered
frostily. Staring up at them, Sara took her bear-
ings from the constellation which she knew as the

Plough and from that she found the North Star.
Then she looked along the road that twisted towards the west between dark, snow-covered crags
of rock. Against the darkness of the sky she could
see the faint loom of light which meant there was
some form of habitation.

'We'll go that way,' she said, turning to Janos
as he joined her on the road. 'We won't have to
walk very far.'

'I hope you are right,' he said goodhumouredly.
'Already my feet are wet. Would you like me to
carry your case?'

'No. No, thank you. I can manage perfectly
well, and you have your own to carry.'

'Then let us link arms and help each other
along. The snow is thick on the road. No cars
have been this way since it started to fall.'

'It's almost as if . . .' Sara broke off, a little self-
conscious about a sudden flight of fancy she was
experiencing.

'Almost as if what?' queried Janos.

'You won't laugh if I tell you?' she asked cautiously.

'How do I know if I'll laugh or not until you
do tell me?' he argued. 'You see, I was right—you
are inhibited. You keep putting a brake on your
feelings and thoughts. Now what were you going
to say?'

'It's almost as if we're in a dream place.' She
stopped in her tracks, suddenly worried. 'I am
conscious, aren't I, Janos?' she whispered. 'I'm
not still knocked out?'

'I believe you are conscious,' he replied seriously, then with humour lightening his voice, 'But it is possible I am knocked out too and we are both having this dream. Perhaps we dream the same dreams, Sara. Perhaps we are intended to share the same dreams,' he went on softly.

'Now you're talking nonsense,' she retorted, and began to walk again. Romantic, beautiful nonsense, her thoughts ran on. The sort of nonsense she had often longed to hear from a man, but most of the men she had known had been incapable of expressing such fanciful thoughts; had been, like herself, inhibited.

Arm in arm they tramped along the snow-covered road. Apart from the sound of water rushing down nearby hillsides it was quiet. Against the starlit sky white slopes glinted occasionally. The air was crisp and cold and their breaths made little clouds of vapour in front of their faces.

'Does it snow in Hungary?' asked Sara, thinking it was a good time for her to find out more about him.

'Sometimes.'

'Did it snow where you lived?'

'In Budapest? Yes, it snowed there. We used to go out to the Buda hills to ski.'

'Budapest must be an interesting city.'

'It has a charm all its own,' he admitted slowly. 'And anyone like you going to it for the first time is likely to fall in love with it at once. There is poetry and romance in its old buildings and in its history. But there is hard, twentieth-century reality in its factories and noisy traffic. It is a place of contrasts, strong but tender, possessing a warm liveliness which is entirely Hungarian and which nothing on this earth can stamp out.'

He spoke with certain pride and vigour and he could have been describing himself, or what she knew of him, she thought. Strong yet tender, warm and lively.

'You must have been sorry to leave it,' she commented.

'No, I was not sorry.'

'Why did you choose to come to Britain?'

'I have told you—to see Cecilia.' Again amusement lilted through his voice. 'Saint Cecilia is the patron of music and musicians, you know.'

'I know. But what are you going to do here? How are you going to make your living?'

'By playing the violin. I am the best violinist in Hungary, in the whole of eastern Europe. Maybe I can be the best violinist in the world,' he replied.

'Well,' Sara couldn't help laughing, 'you're certainly not slow to blow your own trumpet!'

'It is the violin I play, not the trumpet,' Janos retorted. 'And I have a feeling you are now making fun of me. Explain, please.'

'It's an expression we use when someone boasts about their ability.'

'So you think I was boasting, hmm? Not so. I *am* the best violinist. My technique is perfect and one day I will be compared with Paganini and

Heifetz. All I need is the freedom to perform as I want to perform. I did not have that in my own country.'

'Why not?'

He did not answer at once and as they walked along in silence Sara guessed why he was reluctant to tell her.

'It's all right, Janos,' she said softly. 'You can tell me. There's no one here listening in to what you have to say.'

'I was not allowed to make any progress because my parents had been involved in a counter-revolution. I have never been allowed to perform as a soloist. I always had to be a member of a quartet or some other ensemble and when I travelled abroad, especially to countries in the West, I was always watched in case I tried to defect.'

'Are your parents still alive?' she asked.

'I don't know. They were taken away. That is why I lived with my grandparents. My grandmother died two years ago, my grandfather last year. Before he died he advised me to leave Hungary and come West, to make for myself a career. Meeting Cecilia and some other British musicians in Salzburg made me come to a decision. They said they would help me if I came here.'

'But in what way could Cecilia help you?'

He seemed to hesitate before replying, then he said quietly,

'She knows important people in music here.'

Sara was silent, amazed by what he had told

her. What important people in music did Cecilia know? Only her teachers at the college of music she had attended. She must have been showing off when she had told Janos she knew important people in music, and now it was becoming very clear why she didn't want him to arrive at Stonethwaite. She didn't want him to put her promise to the test in front of Philip and his relatives. She was afraid of being exposed as a liar and a show-off.

The road began to slope upwards, seeming to rise to the stars. At the top of the crest light spilled out of the windows of a long low building. Above a plain black door set in thick whitewashed walls hung a wooden sign on which there was painted a picture of a bird with colourful tail feathers. Over the picture were printed the words THE PHEASANT INN.

'This isn't the inn I was thinking of,' said Sara as they approached the door, 'but it seems to be open, thank goodness.'

A brass doorknob turned under her hand and she pushed the door open and walked into a large low-beamed room with a bar at one end and a stone hearth at the other. Warmth from the blazing fire, golden light from chintz-covered wall lamps greeted her. There was no one sitting on any of the old wooden settles, dark with age and shiny from much use, which were set about the floor, and she thought there was no one in the room until someone spoke from behind the bar as Janos closed the door.

'Evening,' said the small grey-haired man who was polishing glasses with a tea-towel. 'I won't call it good,' he added with a twinkle in his small blue eyes. 'Has it stopped snowing yet?'

'Yes,' said Sara, going towards the bar and setting down her case. 'We've had an accident. The car skidded and went off the road. Could we stay the night here? Do you do bed and breakfast?'

'The season doesn't usually open until Easter, but considering the circumstances I won't turn you away,' the small man said with a smile. 'How far down the road is your car?'

'About a mile,' she replied. Janos had put down his case and had gone over to the fire where he squatted down to warm his ungloved hands. 'I thought we couldn't be far from The Coach and Horses at Middlerigg,' she whispered, leaning over the counter,' I haven't noticed this inn before.'

'Well, that's hardly surprising,' said the man with a grin. 'You're not on the road that goes through Middlerigg. You're past that and on the old road which goes through the moors and the fells to Ullswater, past Millwater Lake. You've taken the wrong turning. Where are ye bound for?'

Sara glanced over her shoulder to make sure Janos wasn't within hearing distance and said quietly,

'Stonethwaite.'

'Ye'd have done better if ye'd gone along the M6,' said the innkeeper. 'They keep that pretty clear in this weather.' There was a noise behind him, a door opened and a woman shorter than he was, with a pretty pink and white face and a lot of fuzzy dark hair, appeared. 'Maggie,' he said, 'can we put this lady and gentleman up for the night? Their car's stuck in a drift down the road.'

The woman's glance went from Sara to Janos who was coming away from the fire towards the bar.

'Of course we can,' she said genially. 'I expect ye'd like something to eat too.'

'If that's possible,' said Sara.

'I'll go and put the soup on to heat right away. It's oxtail—made it meself this morning. And there'll be a wedge of chicken and ham pie to follow. Will that suit you?' asked the woman.

'Sounds wonderful,' said Sara, relieved to find the innkeepers so obliging.

'Then perhaps you'll just sign your names in the book,' said the man, producing a register. Sara signed her name and slid the book along to Janos with the pen.

'Do you have a phone I could use?' she asked.

'Go through that door into the hall,' said the man, pointing. 'You'll find a small office on the right. The phone is in there.'

Sara found her way to the cluttered office and closed the door. The phone was in order and soon she was listening to Aunt Hilda's voice.

'Hello, Aunty. It's me, Sara.'

'Thank heaven. Where are you?'

'At the Pheasant Inn.'

'Where? I'm sorry, Sara, but the line is bad and I can't hear you very well.'

'Near Millwater. The car went off the road and . . .'

'Millwater? Good heavens, what on earth are you doing there? You're miles out of your way!'

'I know. It's a long story which I can't tell you now. I just rang to let you know I'm all right, but I won't be able to get to the wedding tomorrow. It may be afternoon by the time the car is on the road again. Will you tell Cecilia I'm sorry I'll miss the ceremony?'

'Well, I'm sure I don't know what you're doing in that part of the Lakes,' her aunt remarked dryly. 'You'd think you'd know your way here by now.'

'I . . . I came this way because I have a . . . a friend with me and he . . . I mean, I wanted to show him something of the scenery. He hasn't been to England before.'

'A friend? What friend?' exclaimed Aunt Hilda.' And why show him the scenery when it's thick with snow? I thought *you* had more sense!'

'His name is Janos. Cecilia knows him. Please tell her he's here with me, Aunty, and that we're both sorry we won't be able to get to the wedding in time, but we both send our best wishes to her and Philip.'

'Very well.' The line was crackling badly now and Aunt Hilda's voice sounded very faint. 'Come as soon as you can.'

'I will. I'm hanging up now because I can't hear

you any more,' Sara shouted into the mouthpiece.

She set down the receiver with a sigh of relief, her duty done. At least they wouldn't be worrying about her now. She went back to the bar room. Janos was sitting on one of the settles by the fire. On the table in front of him were two glasses containing some golden liquid.

'I ordered cognac for you,' he said. 'I thought you might need it after the walk through the snow. Mr Kent, the innkeeper, says we can have our meal in here, by the fire.' He glanced round the cosy room. 'This is a good place,' he added. 'And they are good people. We will be comfortable here tonight.'

'I hope so,' said Sara, picking up her glass and avoiding his intent sultry glance as the memory of the way they had kissed in the car surged into her mind.

'Did you talk to Cecilia on the phone?' he asked.

'No, I talked to my aunt.' She took a sip of the brandy and decided the time had come to warn him about Cecilia. 'I think I should tell you, Janos, you might not see Cecilia tomorrow.'

'Why not?'

'It might be difficult to get the car on the road again,' she began. 'And . . .'

'But we will get help here,' he interrupted her. 'Mr Kent says he has a vehicle with a four-wheel-drive and he will pull your car on to the road. He says the snow will melt tomorrow and all the roads will be clear.' He looked down at his empty glass

and frowned slightly, then gave her a curious
glance. 'Why did you come this way, Sara?' he
asked softly. 'Mr Kent says it is not the way to
Stonethwaite. Did you hope we would be
delayed? Did you hope to spend some more time
with me as I wished I could spend more time with
you? Did you hope to spend the night alone with
me?'

'No, oh, no,' she said quickly. 'That wasn't the
reason at all. 'She leaned forward across the small
table to whisper so that Mr Kent who was still
polishing glasses at the bar couldn't hear what she
was saying. 'I've told you. Just because I kissed
you you mustn't get ideas about me. It meant
nothing.'

His dark eyebrows lifted in satiric surprise and
his eyes glinted with mockery.

'Am I to believe then that you are the sort of
woman who goes around kissing men for fun? Are
you a flirt? Do you intend to lead me on as you
have led on Mr Caldwell?'

'I haven't led Tom on,' she retorted angrily.
'And I'm not leading you on.'

'Then why have you gone to so much trouble
to arrange for us to be delayed on the way to
Stonethwaite? Why don't you want me to see
Cecilia again?' he asked, and his eyes were no
longer the colour of tawny sherry but were hard
and cold like iced amber.

'I . . . she . . . oh, I don't know how to tell you,'
she muttered, relieved to see Mrs Kent coming
across the room carrying a tray. The woman set

the tray down on another table and carried two bowls of steaming soup over, setting them before them. She brought a basket of hot bread rolls, and a dish of butter.

'There you are,' she said cheerfully. 'Enjoy the soup. I'll bring the pie and salad when you've finished it. Would you like coffee or tea?'

'Tea, please,' said Sara. Janos shook his head and said he would have nothing else to drink.

As she picked up a roll and broke it Sara watched Janos do the same from under her lashes, hoping he wouldn't press her to answer his question about Cecilia. But he seemed more interested in satisfying his hunger than in asking her awkward questions and they ate the delicious hot soup in silence. The outside door opened and some men came in, laughing and talking, stamping the snow from their feet. After glancing curiously at Sara and Janos they clustered round the bar to order beer.

Janos finished his soup first, then leaned back in his chair. Although she kept her eyes lowered Sara knew he was watching her and felt herself growing tense. At last, unable to stand his silent appraisal any longer, she put down her soup spoon and raising a hand to her head stood up.

'Excuse me,' she murmured. 'My head is hurting. I think I'll find Mrs Kent and ask her to show me to my room.'

'Forgive me.' Janos was on his feet instantly and coming round to her. 'I had forgotten you had been hurt.' Eyes dark now with concern, he

raised a hand and touched the bump on her forehead. His fingers lingered suggestively, sliding
down in a subtle caress over her temple, and her
knees shook. 'I'll come with you,' he offered,
taking hold of her arm.

'No, no.' Sara pulled her arm free of his grasp.
'Please stay here and finish your meal. I'll be all
right once I've had a good night's rest. Please,
Janos, don't worry. Stay here.'

'You are sure?'

'I'm sure. Goodnight,' she said firmly, and
walked away over to the bar. 'I'd like to go up to
my room now,' she said to Mr Kent.

'Go right to the kitchen, lass,' he said. 'You'll
find Maggie there. She'll show you the way.'

In the small but brightly lit kitchen Maggie
Kent was filling a rubber hot water bottle.

'Have you finished your soup?' she asked.

'Yes, but I've decided not to have anything else
to eat,' said Sara, touching the bump on her head
again. 'I don't feel very well. My head aches, so I
thought I'd go to bed. Do you have any aspirin?'

'Aye, I do.' Mrs Kent produced a bottle of pills
and filled a glass with water. Sara took two of the
pills. 'I thought you might want to turn in early,
so I was filling a hot water bottle for you,' said
Mrs Kent. 'Your case is already upstairs. Would
you like me to come up with you?'

'No, thanks,' said Sara, taking the hot water
bottle. 'Just tell me where the room is.'

'It's the second door on the landing to your
right.'

The room was small and had a sloping ceiling. The walls were covered with rose-patterned paper and it was furnished with a chest of drawers, two chairs and two single beds with old-fashioned brass ends. Sara found the bathroom, and after a quick wash she returned to the bedroom and shut the door firmly. There was no lock.

Pleased with herself because she had managed to get away from Janos for a while, she undressed, slipped into her nightgown and slid into one of the beds, cuddling the hot water bottle against her.

Tomorrow would be soon enough to tell Janos that he could not see Cecilia. Maybe by then she would have thought up a way of telling him without hurting his feelings too much. And surely he would see there was no point in him going to Stonethwaite with her once he knew Cecilia wouldn't be there.

She reached out and switched off the light over the bed and snuggling down closed her eyes. Immediately darkness swirled about her and she imagined she was back in the car with Janos's arms around her, his lips against hers. Her heart was beating fast and passion was flooding through her in a hot tide, while the hauntingly romantic melody of the second movement of the Brahms Violin Concerto sang sweetly through her head.

CHAPTER THREE

A LONG note held on the solo violin brought the second movement to an end. Sara opened her eyes, surprised to find herself not in bed at the inn but in the concert hall where the audience, having held itself back from clapping, was whispering during the short pause before the third movement began. Again the conductor raised his arms, his baton swept down and Janos began to play a series of vibrant chords, filling the auditorium with the beautiful, lively music which he loved so much and could interpret so well.

Sara closed her eyes again, yet she could still see him in her mind's eye. He was not on the stage, nor was he wearing formal black and white. He was standing between the two single beds in the small bedroom at the Pheasant Inn and was wearing only his trousers. Beneath the dusky gold of his bare skin the muscles in his arms and shoulders rippled and his gypsy-black hair leapt out from his head as he played the same wild yet sweet chords.

Surprised by the sight of him silhouetted against the bright sunlight which was streaming into the room through the dormer window, she sat up in bed, pushing her hair back from her brow. Seeing her move, he stopped playing at once, breaking off in mid-chord and, violin in hand, sat down on the side of the bed, close to her, his brightly-dark glance going over her.

'At last you wake up,' he said. 'I was worried about you. You sleep so heavily, so still. You were asleep when I came to bed and you did not move all night.'

Sara looked at the other bed. It was rumpled, the pillow creased and dented and out of position, the bed clothes thrown back. She looked at him accusingly.

'You slept in this room?' she demanded.

'Yes. Where else would I sleep?' he countered. 'This is the room to which Mrs Kent sent me.'

'I don't believe you. I don't believe she sent you to this room. Why would she? She knows we're single persons. I don't believe she told you this was the room where you would sleep. You found out where I was and you decided you'd sleep in here with me!'

Janos stared at her blankly for a moment, then said quietly,

'If you don't believe me you can ask Mrs Kent.' He laid down his violin and bow, shifted closer to her and took both of her hands in his. 'What is it, Sara? Why are you so angry? Does your head still hurt?' he asked softly.

'No, it doesn't.' She tried to pull her hands from his, but his long muscular fingers gripped strongly. 'Why didn't you ask Mrs Kent for another room?' she asked, avoiding his glance, a little afraid of the way he was looking at her and yet excited too.

'Because I wanted to be near you in the night,' he murmured, leaning closer so that she was suddenly aware of the healthy male scents of his skin and hair. 'I thought you might not feel well and it is good to have someone with you when you are not feeling well, to comfort you and hold your hand.' He glanced down at their entwined hands, then he lifted hers one at a time to his lips.

'Please, you mustn't do that,' she protested, pulling her hands free at last.

'Why mustn't I?' he queried, lifting his eyebrows. 'Why shouldn't I show you that I like you and I'm happy to be with you, that I am glad you are feeling better? It is a beautiful morning outside. The sun is shining on the hills so that they glitter like silver against the sky. This is a lovely country and I am glad you have brought me to see it. I am glad to be alive and here with you and that we are going to drive to Stonethwaite together today.'

'If we get the car on the road,' Sara said dryly, and a little shakily, alarmed at the desire which was suddenly leaping through her; a desire to respond to him to say she was also glad to be there with him; a longing to frame his face with her hands and kiss him. Never in all her twenty-four years had she felt like this about a man. 'Janos, please go and ask Mr Kent if he can pull the car out of the snow bank,' she whispered. 'Please go away, out of the room. I ... I'd like to get dressed.'

'And I would like to stay and watch you,' he

murmured, his glance shifting to her throat and downwards to the shape of her breasts under the thin clinging nightgown. 'You are lovely in the morning, Sara, even with a bruise on your forehead.' Laughter glinted in his eyes as they lifted to meet hers. 'I wish I could see you in bed every morning,' he added in a whisper, and bending his head swiftly kissed her on the mouth.

There was no resistance in her, although her hands did go to his shoulders as if to push him away. But they didn't push. Instead her fingers spread out over the smooth hardness, finding their way instinctively to the vulnerable hollows in his spine, caressingly, coaxingly, then somehow he was on the bed with her and they were entwined closely, kissing deeply and thirstily, both of them oblivious of time and place. How long they might have stayed there, how far they might have gone along the sensuous path towards the culmination of passion, Sara was not to know. A sudden knock on the bedroom door made them both start and stiffen and pull away from each other.

'Yes?' she called out. 'Who is it?'

'Maggie Kent. George is ready to go in the Land Rover to pull your car out of the snowdrift and he'd like one of you to go with him. Perhaps your husband will go. He says your car might not start and if he has to tow it he'd like someone to steer it.'

Her husband! Sara stared accusingly at Janos. His eyes glinted with amusement as he returned her stare, then he called out,

'All right, Mrs Kent, I'll go. I won't be long.'

He slid off the bed, stood up and went over to the chair where he had laid his clothes. Picking up his shirt, he began to slip it on.

'How could you!' Sara found her voice was hoarse with the anger which was raging through her. 'How could you tell her we . . . that we . . . that you . . .?' Speech deserted her and she could only glare at him.

'That we are married?' he finished for her blandly, turning to look at her as he pulled on his suit jacket. 'I did not tell her that. She assumed it.'

'But why? Why should she assume it? We signed different names in the register.'

'No, we didn't. I signed the same name as you.'

'You——' Again she was speechless, amazed at his affrontery. 'Oh, really,' she went on faintly. 'You had no right to do that without telling me. Why did you do it?'

'I did it for the best,' he replied serenely, sliding an arm into the sleeve of his trenchcoat. 'To stop them from asking too many questions.' The trenchcoat on, he came towards the bed, where Sara was sitting upright, a picture of offended dignity. Shadowed by their long lashes, his brilliant eyes gazed right into hers. 'I wanted them to believe we are married so that they would give us a room to share. I wanted to be near you,' he added softly.

Unable to sustain the blatant desire expressed in his eyes, she looked down at her hands which were clenched on the bedcover.

'Are you sure that was the only reason?' she challenged sharply.

'What other reason could there be?' he said, and seemed genuinely surprised by her question.

'You could be in this country illegally,' she accused. 'You could be here without a passport or a visa and want to hide your real identity from the authorities in case they deport you. You could have been smuggled in.'

His mouth curved into a slightly mocking smile as, still gazing into her eyes, he sat down on the edge of the bed, close to her again.

'You're quite right, I could have been smuggled in,' he agreed. 'But I haven't. My papers are all in order.' He paused, then added as he leaned so close to her his breath wafted her cheek, 'I pretended to be your husband for one reason only—because I want to be with you as much as possible, make love to you . . .'

'Oh, stop it!' she cried, putting her hands over her ears. 'Stop being so . . . so . . . silly!'

'You think it is silly then to be in love?' he asked.

'I think it's silly to talk about being in love when you've known a person for only a day and a half. You're not—you can't be in love with me,' she argued, keeping her eyes cast down to avoid his intent gaze yet aware of a desire to touch him swelling up within her and threatening to burst through her control.

'Can't I? If you hardly know me how can you know anything about the way I feel?' he taunted.

'And what do you know about falling in love? You've never let yourself go enough to fall in love. You're on guard all the time, afraid that someone might take advantage of you. What is the matter with you, Sara? Why are you so afraid of me? Will it help you to relax if I tell you that never have I taken a woman against her will? Making love is a shared pleasure, or should be. It isn't worthy of being described as making love if it doesn't give pleasure to both the people involved.' He touched her cheek with gentle fingers, then stood up. 'But I must go and help Mr Kent.'

He left the room. Her fingers touching and exploring her lips which still throbbed from his kisses, Sara flopped back against the pillows, giving way to the amazement she was feeling. Surely she was dreaming? She must be experiencing some wild erotic fantasy as a result of being banged on the head. It must be a dream, because never in her right mind would she have behaved as she had just behaved with Janos. Never would she let a man she had only just met kiss and fondle her as he had done, and never would she have encouraged him by kissing and caressing him.

Falling in love—was that what she was doing? Her lips curled derisively. She had never had time for such romantic nonsense, had never discussed it with other girls and had never imagined it happening to herself. At least, not as swiftly as a snap of the fingers. Then why had she let Janos kiss her and why had she responded so wholeheartedly? Because she had sensed a hunger in him for comfort, a hunger which she had longed to satisfy in some way; because she found him attractive physically; because she was fascinated by his difference from the other men she had known and she wanted to know him better.

Impatient suddenly with the direction in which her thoughts were straying, she sat up, flung back the sheets and blankets and slid off the bed. Going over to the window, she looked out at a view of sunlit, snow-sprinkled fields sloping away to distant sharp-edged mountains which glittered like silver against a pale sky. Cradled between dark green conifers and the bare branches of birches a small lake twinkled cobalt blue and nearer at hand, puddles forming on the surface of the road glinted with azure and gold light. The sound of water was everywhere as snow melted, dripping from the low eaves of the roof, rushing and gurgling in streams down the hillsides.

Sara glanced at her watch, surprised to see that it was almost ten o'clock. In an hour from now Cecilia would arrive at the parish church at Stonethwaite to be married to Philip. In another two hours they would be leaving the reception held at the old country inn opposite the church to drive to Prestwick airport to catch a trans-Atlantic jet. Stonethwaite was not much more than forty-five miles away and if her car was all right she could be there in time to see them off. But only if she could get rid of Janos, only if she could leave him here so that Cecilia would not have to meet him.

Feeling the air cold on her skin, she shivered

and began to look for clothes to wear. She dressed in well-cut grey worsted pants instead of the tweed skirt she had worn the day before and topped them with a high-necked black sweater that clung to her figure. She swept her hair up on top of her head and pinned it there in a casual chignon so that loose ends curved attractively about her neck and cheeks. Then she packed her suitcase and taking it with her went downstairs.

After informing her that her husband had already had his breakfast Mrs Kent served her bacon and eggs and tea in the bar-parlour. Sara was just finishing the meal when she heard the Land Rover pull up outside the inn, and putting on her sheepskin jacket, she went out. Behind the Land Rover was the Mini, being towed. Janos was sitting behind its steering wheel.

'What's wrong with the car?' asked Sara, turning to George Kent as he stepped down from his vehicle.

'It's cold and damp after spending the night in the snowdrift. It'll be right enough when it's dried out,' he replied, bending to unshackle the chain with which he had towed the car.

'How long will that take?'

'A couple of hours, with a bit of luck. I'll push it into the shed and put a fan heater under the hood. That should do the trick. You and your hubby are welcome to wait in the inn.'

'I'm afraid we're going to be delayed much longer than I'd thought,' Sara said to Janos as they went into the inn again.

'It doesn't matter.' He shrugged fatalistically. 'What will be will be. And now I have time to practise.'

'Practise?' she repeated, following him across the room to the stairs.

'Yes. I should practise the violin every day, but for the last few days that has not been possible. Now there is time while we wait for your car to dry out. Excuse me.' He spoke with a cool politeness, which pushed her away, and went up the stairs.

In the bar-parlour Sara sat by the window watching the sunbeams dance on the puddles in the road. From above the sound of the violin floated down to her as Janos played one scale after another, then wove the scales into melodies, some of them sweet and tuneful and some of them harsh and discordant.

If the car had been going she could have left now while he was absorbed in practising. She could have gone without him knowing. On sudden impulse she left the inn and went to the shed. Sliding behind the steering wheel of the Mini, she turned the key in the ignition. The engine coughed a little and then died whiningly. She tried to start it again and the same thing happened. Was it a good sign? Did it mean that everything was drying out? Or should she find a mechanic to fix it?

Back in the inn she looked for Mrs Kent and found her in the kitchen cleaning out a cupboard, humming in tune to the music which was pouring down like liquid gold from the bedroom upstairs.

'My goodness,' Mrs Kent exclaimed when she saw Sara, 'that husband of yours can certainly play! He must have magic in his fingers.'

Or be in league with the devil, thought Sara, remembering a story she had once read about the great violinist Paganini who had played difficult pieces of music with such ease that a critic had said he must be in league with the devil.

'Is there a garage near here?' she asked, suppressing an urge to blurt out that Janos was not her husband.

'Aye. In the village, about a mile from here.'

'Is there a mechanic there, someone who could fix the car?'

'I daresay you could call Sam Armstrong who owns the garage a mechanic.'

'Then do you think Mr Kent would tow my car that far? I'm afraid it's taking much longer to dry out than I'd thought it would. I was hoping to be at Stonethwaite by one o'clock. I'm going to miss seeing my cousin if I don't get there before then.'

'It's a pity you didn't think to ask George to do that when he brought the car here,' said Mrs Kent. 'He's gone out. He left a few minutes ago to drive into Kendal and he won't be back until four. But I'm sure your car will dry out. You can use the phone again, if you like, to get in touch with your people and ask them to wait for you.'

'Thank you.'

Sara went back to the bar-room. There wasn't any point in phoning her aunt or Cecilia; they

would both be in church. Sitting down near the
window again, she tried to imagine the wedding
scene, but couldn't because the music Janos was
playing was totally alien to any marriage ceremony
performed in the Church of England. It was full
of wild chords which were often discordant, and
yet it leapt and sang with a strong dancing
rhythm, and she guessed it was a Hungarian folk
dance.

Magic in his fingers—Mrs Kent was right. His
technique was amazing. But there was more to
his playing than the ability to hit the right notes
quickly and accurately. And he didn't play like a
devil, he played like an angel- a dark fallen angel,
perhaps, one who knew all about the passion and
suffering, about the violent side of life as well as
its beauty and joyousness. And all that he knew,
all that he was came through in his playing.

The dance came to an end. There was silence.
Sara rose to her feet and went upstairs. Now that
it was almost twelve-thirty and too late for them
to see Cecilia it was time to tell Janos he was not
going to see her.

She went into the bedroom. Janos was putting
his violin in its case. He glanced round at her.

'Is the car working now?' he asked. Sweat
gleamed on his face and his black hair was dis-
hevelled. He looked as if he had expended a lot of
energy.

'No, it isn't. I'm afraid we're going to miss
Cecilia.'

'Miss her?' He looked puzzled.

'By the time the car has dried out and we're able to leave here she'll have left Stonethwaite. She'll be on her way to California.'

In the process of re-waxing his violin bow, he paused to stare at her, his eyes wide and golden.

'California?' he repeated. 'Why is she going there?'

'To live with her husband.'

Still staring at her, he sank down on the bed behind him.

'You are telling me Cecilia is married?' he demanded hoarsely.

'Yes.'

'When? When did she get married?' He rapped the question at her, his voice clearing, and there was a strange glitter in his eyes as he continued to stare at her from under frowning eyebrows.

'This morning—a few minutes ago. That's why I was going to Stonethwaite, to be at the wedding. She'd invited me,' Sara explained quickly, trying not to feel alarmed by the way Janos was staring at her. The eagle look was back in his eyes and he seemed to be assessing her in a predatory way. She turned away to the window, afraid of that look. 'Now I won't even get there in time to wish her well before she leaves,' she added. 'I'm very disappointed.'

'I'm sure you are.' He laughed shortly and she whirled to glance at him warily. Had he guessed she had delayed him deliberately? He wasn't staring at her any more. He was looking down at the violin bow and all she could see was the top of his head, the way the black hair sprang vigorously up from a central parting as if it had a life of its own. 'But I am not disappointed,' he added softly as if speaking to himself.

'What will you do now?' she asked.

He looked up slowly. The glitter had faded from his eyes and their glance was soft, dangerously sensual as it met hers briefly, then drifted downwards over her face and her figure and his mouth curved into a mischievous smile.

'I shall wait here with you until your car starts,' he said quietly, and rising to his feet he went over to the violin case to place the bow in it.

'But surely, now that you know Cecilia isn't at Stonethwaite you won't want to go there? If she isn't in this country she can't give you the help she promised, can she?' said Sara, following him across the room.

'That is true, she can't,' he said, snapping the locks on the violin case and putting it in his suitcase. He sighed and added, 'It is a good thing there are others I can ask for help. But I trusted her. She seemed honest. She seemed to mean what she said.'

'Oh, I'm so sorry.' It burst out of her spontaneously as a feeling which was more than sympathy, more than regret for the way her cousin had behaved, swept through her in a warm surge. 'Cecilia is sometimes very silly. She shows off and says things she doesn't mean. But she didn't believe you would ever come to this country.'

'How do you know that?' Janos swung round

to face her and his eyes seemed to stab right into hers. Too late she realised she had said too much in her attempt to excuse her cousin. 'I thought you said she had never told you about me and had never discussed our meeting in Salzburg,' he added, stepping towards her and standing over her, his hands on his hips. 'So you did talk to her last night on the phone.'

'No, I didn't. It was . . .' She broke off, catching her lower lip between her teeth.

'Don't lie to me any more, Sara,' he said, his voice deepening and softening as his hands reached out to her shoulders. 'I don't want there to be any lies between us to spoil our friendship.'

'I phoned Cecilia on Thursday night,' she whispered, swaying slightly towards him, unable to take her fascinated glance away from his mouth, trapped suddenly by a flare-up of physical attraction between them. 'After you'd fallen asleep,' she added, wanting now, more than anything else, for everything to be straight and open between them, for there to be no more deceit. 'I told her you'd arrived at the flat and asked her if she wanted to see you. She asked me to prevent you from going to Stonethwaite. I tried to put you off, but you insisted on going. So I asked you to come with me thinking I could delay you until she had gone away with Philip.' Seeing a strange expression flicker in his eyes, and guessing he was hurt she cried out urgently, 'Oh, I'm so sorry, Janos. I'm sorry Cecilia let you down.'

'You don't have to apologise for her,' he told

her. 'I made the mistake of thinking that she meant what she said in Salzburg.' His hands slid over her shoulders caressingly as he drew her towards him. Her hands went out to flatten against his bared chest, ostensibly to hold him away but instead softening, the fingers curling and groping with sensuous delight when they felt his warm hair-crisped skin.

'But I'm not just apologising for Cecilia,' she persisted. 'I'm sorry I deceived you.'

'You didn't deceive me,' he whispered, raising a hand and sliding his fingers between the close-fitting high neck of her sweater and her throat, touching delicately the vulnerable hollow where her pulse beat fast. 'I guessed there was some trick behind your suggestion that I should travel with you.'

'You did? Then why did you come with me?' she gasped, tipping her head back to look at him and finding that his lips were very close to hers.

'I came with you because I wanted to come with you. I wanted to be with you and I still want to be with you. But now I don't have any excuse to go any farther with you, because Cecilia won't be at Stonethwaite.' He paused and his lips nibbled at the corner of her mouth. 'Do you still have to go to Stonethwaite?' he asked softly. 'Couldn't we stay here another night?'

Sara's senses were reeling out of her control. Somewhere at the back of her mind a still small voice warned her that she should not let her emotions get the better of her, but it was soon smothered as new sensations swept through her when Janos's hand curved to the swell of her breast.

'We—I don't have to go to Stonethwaite any more now that Cecilia won't be there,' she said impulsively, her hands sliding up and round his neck. 'We could stay here another night. I want to be with you, too,' she added in a shy whisper, letting the warm rush of feeling break through, giving in at last to an instinctive desire to love him no matter who he was or where he had come from. And as his lips claimed hers she knew that she would never be the same. The cool self-contained guarded Sara had gone for ever, and the ice which had frozen her emotions for so long had been broken and had melted away at the first touch of his passion.

'And afterwards when we go back to Manchester we will make my dream come true?' he asked, lifting his mouth from hers framing her face with long gentle fingers, gazing into her eyes with eyes that blazed like topazes between jet black lashes.

'What dream?' she faltered.

'The dream I have had for the past twenty-four hours, that we are married. I would like very much for us to be really married, Sara. Tell me you would like it too.'

'I would like it, too,' she murmured dazedly. It was happening to her, actually happening to her. This being from another world, with magic in his fingers, was asking her to marry him!

'When? Soon? The day after tomorrow?' He

was suddenly urgent.

'No—oh no!' she was laughing. 'We can't marry as soon as that. It isn't possible.'

'Why not? Is there someone you must ask? Do I have to get permission from your aunt and uncle?'

'No. The only person you have to ask is me, and you've already done that and I've said yes. But we have to give notice to the registrar of marriages of our intention to get married, and then we'll have to wait three weeks.'

'So long?' Janos frowned impatiently. 'In that time you could change your mind.'

'I've told you that once I make up my mind I don't change it,' she reminded him. 'Anyway, you could change your mind too.'

'But I won't.' His arms encircled her again. 'Please forgive my impatience, Sara,' he whispered into the thickness of her hair. 'It is becoming difficult for me to be in the same place as you without making love to you. I want you—I want you so much it is beginning to hurt.'

'It's beginning to hurt me too,' she murmured, pressing against him, trying to imprint her shape on his. 'And I'll marry you as soon as it's possible and together we'll make our dream come true.'

From then on time and other people became of no account to them. There was no hurry to go to Stonethwaite or anywhere else that day and they had no desire to be with anyone else as long as they were together, and next morning it was with a certain reluctance that they left the little inn among the hills and made the return journey to Manchester.

Janos stayed the Sunday night at the flat with her and the next day they went together to the registrar's office to make arrangements for their marriage in three weeks' time. When that was done Sara drove him to the station to catch a train to London where, he had told her, he had an appointment with Gareth Williams, the conductor of a well-known English string orchestra, whom he had met once in Austria.

Parting from him after being so close to him for three days hurt more than Sara had expected, and as she made her way to the design offices of Ferris Fabrics she found herself wondering again if she were experiencing a fantasy. Perhaps all that had happened to her recently was a figment of her imagination, the result of a subconscious longing to love and be loved. Perhaps Janos didn't exist at all but was merely someone she had invented, designed and created by her and made up of all the characteristics she had secretly hoped to find one day in a man; the man she would love and marry.

It was Tom Caldwell who reassured her that Janos was real. When she looked into his office he asked her if she had had a good weekend. Not wanting him to know what had actually happened, she answered vaguely,

'Everything went off according to plan.'

'And what about the Hungarian chap?' he asked. 'Did he stay in Stonethwaite?'

'No. He . . . he's gone to London, for an interview.'

She changed the subject then, referring to a design problem, but inwardly she had known a sense of relief. Janos did exist. Tom had met him and remembered him.

Janos did not return until Friday. He was waiting by the car when she left the mill offices. Their meeting was restrained, both of them being too aware of other people around them in the car park to show their delight in seeing each other. Only by the sudden golden blaze in his eyes and by the hard pressure of his fingers on her hand did Sara know he was glad to be there with her. Only by smiling at him and returning the pressure of his fingers could she reveal her relief and pleasure that he had come back to her. And although the afternoon was dull and dreary dark clouds threatening rain as usual it seemed to Sara that everything about the busy city streets through which she drove to the flat was suddenly beautiful, outlined in a magical glowing light.

Once in the privacy of the flat both of them had no hesitation in indulging their feelings and giving full expression to their joy at being together again. She went willingly into Janos's outstretched arms and for a long time there was silence as with lips and hands they worshipped each other.

Later they talked. His news was good and he was elated. Gareth Williams had promised him a position in the violin section of the orchestra and he would start rehearsing with the orchestra soon after their wedding.

'Is it what you wanted?' Sara asked.

'It is a beginning, a step in the right direction,' he replied. 'Once it is known how well I play I will be given the leadership of the orchestra and will perform any violin solos. The orchestra makes many recordings and often goes on concert tours. I will soon become famous and will be asked to perform at concerts with other orchestras.'

His lack of modesty where his ability was concerned, his calm assumption that he would become famous, amused Sara, and she teased him about it. In retaliation he tickled her and tried to kiss her. Laughingly she escaped from him. Janos chased her, catching up with her in her bedroom and, pulling her into his arms. They lost balance and fell across the bed, where for a while they made love again, finding pleasure in exciting new sensations in each other.

Slowly the dark blue dusk of the April evening darkened the room. Lying on the bed, intimately entwined with each other, they talked softly and intermittently, pausing to kiss each other often.

'Do you still want to marry me two weeks from now?' Janos whispered, twinging his fingers in her hair.

'Yes, I still want to marry you.'

'I told Gareth I am going to marry an English girl. He said it was a good idea and wished us well.' His arms tightened about her and he buried his face against her throat. The flicker of his eyelashes against her skin sent tingles of delight coursing along her nerves. 'Thank God I met you, Sara,' Janos murmured. 'I do not know what I would have done if you had not been here the night I came and if you had not been so kind and generous and made me welcome.'

Pressed closely against him, she was tantalised by the scents of his skin and hair, and a fierce longing to touch, taste and smell every part of him blasted through her, destroying her control over herself. Ablaze with desire, she pulled at the buttons of his shirt until they were undone. Her face buried against his chest, she licked the saltiness of his skin while her nails dug into the smooth muscled curves of his bared shoulders until he gasped. His hand came up and tipped her head back roughly so he could ravage her mouth with his, and once more they became oblivious to everything except their need for each other.

'We must make the most of this time together,' he said later. 'Once I am working with the orchestra I will not have much time to be with you. Will you come to London to live with me there? Or would you prefer to stay here?'

'I would prefer to stay here . . . at least for the time being. I don't want to give up my job at Ferris's, I enjoy it too much.'

'I understand. And I would not want you to give it up just to be with me all the time. So for a while we will commute, hmm? I'll come here to stay with you whenever I am free from musical commitments and sometimes you will come to stay with me?'

'Supposing . . . supposing we have a child?' she murmured. 'Would you like us to have a baby, Janos?'

To her surprise he stiffened and rolled away from her to lie on his back. His withdrawal puzzled her and she leaned up on one elbow to peer at him in the darkness, but it was impossible to see the expression on his face.

'What is it?' she said anxiously. 'Don't you like babies? Wouldn't you like us to have a family one day?'

'One day, in the far distant future, perhaps,' he replied, pulling her down on top of him and framing her face with his hands. 'But not yet. Not for a long time,' he went on softly. 'Our times together will be too precious to me and I'll want you all to myself. Selfish of me, I know, but that is the way I am, Sara. Are you disappointed in me? Did you hope for a domesticated husband, one who would stay at home and help you rear a family?'

Was that the sort of husband she had hoped for? She didn't know the answer to his question. But she did know she wanted to be the woman he came back to, to share his spare moments with. She wanted to be the woman he wanted all to himself.

'No, I'm not disappointed in you,' she whispered. 'I love you as you are.'

'Thank you,' he murmured, drawing her face down to his until their lips met in a kiss of such sweet reverence there was no need for words to express how they felt about their forthcoming marriage.

The next two weeks passed by in a blur of happiness for Sara as she went every day to work, returning with excitement every evening to the flat because she knew Janos would be there waiting for her. They were married on a Saturday morning in weather that was typical of April, warm showers interrupted by periods of bright sunshine, and after the simple civil ceremony they drove in the Mini to the coast to spend the night in a small hotel with a view of the sea.

On the Monday morning Janos left for London, promising to let her know where he would be living and when he would come to see her again. After seeing him off Sara went to work, bracing herself to tell Tom Caldwell the news which she had kept from him ever since she had returned from the Lake District.

She waited until it was almost four-thirty and time for leaving work before telling him, in the privacy of his office. After staring at her incredulously for a few seconds he blurted out,

'You fool! You . . . you blithering idiot, letting yourself be conned like that!'

'Conned?' she exclaimed, not understanding him.

'Taken in, then. Tricked into doing something you wouldn't normally have done if you'd been in your right mind.'

'I haven't been taken in,' she retorted.

'No?' Tom came as close to sneering as she had ever seen. 'Of course you have. A handsome stranger with a mysteriously romantic background steps into your life, he turns on the charm and before anyone can snap their fingers you've married him. It isn't the first time it's been done by a foreigner who's wanted to stay in this country.' He ruffled his fair hair with one hand and came across to her, an expression of anxiety on his plain homely face. 'Oh, Sara, I thought you had more common sense than to . . . to fall in love with a penniless adventurer who's probably in this country illegally . . .'

'He isn't. His papers are all in order,' she interrupted him quickly. 'He's been permitted to come here to visit Cecilia and . . . and other people he knows here.'

'But does he have permission to stay and work here?' Tom argued.

'I . . . I . . . er . . . don't know, but I think he must have, because he's been given a job as a violinist in the New Century Orchestra, and you know how prestigious that is. He's gone to London this morning, to join the orchestra.'

'I see. Having got what he wanted—a marriage certificate—he's left you.'

'No, he hasn't left me. We . . . well, since we both have careers which mean a lot to both of us and which make it difficult for us to live in the same place, we're going to commute for a while between here and London.' Sara tilted her chin at him defiantly when she noticed the scepticism expressed on his face. 'It's been done before. In fact it's done quite often, these days.'

'So I've heard,' he remarked jeeringly. 'A marriage of convenience, I suppose you could call it, especially for him.' With a sigh he turned back to his desk. 'But what about your cousin Cecilia? What does she think about you marrying her friend?'

'She doesn't know yet. I haven't told anyone . . . except you.'

'And why haven't you told me before this?' Tom queried, swinging round to look at her again. 'No, don't bother to answer that—I can guess why. You knew I'd warn you against him. My God,' he muttered, leaning his hips against the desk and shaking his head from side to side, 'I'm still finding it hard to believe that you . . . you of all people, Sara the unassailable, so cool and so guarded . . . have fallen for the first fellow with a broken English accent who comes along. Blind as a bat, that's what you are, and he's used you, played on your sympathies, seduced you into . . .'

'That's enough!' She was suddenly very angry with him. 'Anyone would think you were jealous of Janos, to hear you,' she rebuked him sharply.

'I am—I am. He's walked in where I've feared to tread, and snatched you from beneath my nose.'

'But you have no right to feel jealous and no right to criticise me for marrying him. And he isn't what you say he is, a penniless adventurer. He's an extremely gifted and talented musician who's come here to find the freedom to develop in his own way.'

'Granted,' he retorted. 'But that doesn't alter the possibility that he's married you so that he has a reason to stay in this country, so that he can claim some sort of status here and take employment here.'

'What if he has?' Sara flung at him, her head up high. 'If in marrying me he's been able to find the freedom he's been looking for then I'm glad I agreed to marry him. I'm glad I've been able to help someone who's worthy of help.'

'You'll never come first with him, you know,' he taunted. 'He's the type who'll always put his career first, and when he doesn't need your help any more he'll just shove you aside and go on without you . . .'

'Stop it, stop it!' she cried. 'Stop trying to destroy our marriage before it's really begun. Oh, I wish I'd never told you I'd married him!' And whirling round, she left the room, banging the door behind him.

Tom never referred to her married status again and it wasn't long before she was back on the old footing with him, but it was a while before the suspicion that perhaps she had been used by Janos sank to the bottom of her mind and was forgotten. Many times during the next few months when they were together she could have asked him if he had married her so that he could stay in the country and not because he loved her, but she never did, because she was afraid that if she did she might cause the fragile fabric of their marriage to tear and become damaged for ever.

Because it was fragile, their relationship, a beautifully and delicately woven gossamer web in which they had both been caught, and when they were together either at Sara's flat or in the furnished flat which Janos had been able to rent in Chelsea they added more strands of silk to the web, weaving it more tightly about them as they learned about each other.

As time went by and Janos became more and more involved in the musical scene of the capital he came less often to Manchester and Sara visited him more often in London, often attending a concert in which he was performing. She enjoyed such visits and was soon on friendly terms with Ida Williams, the wife of the conductor of the string orchestra.

'I don't know how you can bear to leave Janos here and go back to Manchester,' Ida said one Sunday evening. She and Sara were in the main bedroom of the Williamses' house, where Janos and Sara had been guests for Sunday dinner and Sara was putting on her coat in readiness to go to the station to catch the last train north. 'It must be a terrible strain on you both to be always saying goodbye to each other,' Ida went on. 'And then you must worry about him when you're not with him.'

'About his health, you mean? Or about whether he eats properly or changes his socks every day? Or whether he has a clean shirt to put on?' Sara asked mockingly as she fastened the belt of her coat. 'Do you think I should? He seems to be very well always and I think he's quite tough really and learned at an early age to look after himself. He's an awfully good cook, you know—makes delicious goulash and *paprikascirke*—that's Hungarian for paprika chicken. And if you don't believe me you should come and have dinner with us next time I'm in town and he'll do the cooking. Let's make that a firm invitation for next Saturday. Will you and Gareth come?'

'We'd like to,' said Ida.

'And bring Davina, too.' Davina was the Williamses' only daughter. 'She tells me she's taking lessons from Janos.'

'Yes. It was her own idea. Gareth and I didn't want her to ask Janos. We felt it to be an imposition because already he has several pupils. I only hope he didn't give in to her because she's our daughter and he didn't like to offend Gareth. She's terribly headstrong.'

'And very pretty,' said Sara as she drew on her gloves. Tall and willowy and just seventeen, Davina Williams had a mane of curly midnight black hair hanging to her waist, heavy-lidded dark blue eyes, a pink and white skin and a full-lipped, sensual mouth. When she was in the same room as Janos she sat and stared at him all the time, obviously in the throes of an adolescent crush on him.

'Sara, I don't want you to think I'm interfering,' Ida said thoughtfully, 'but it wasn't Janos's health I was thinking you might worry about. I suppose I'm a bit old-fashioned because I believe a woman should live with her husband if that's at all possible. I mean . . .' Ida broke off and her cheeks coloured faintly with red. 'I'm making a mess of this, aren't I?' she added with a self-disparaging grin. 'What I'm trying to say is . . . well, don't you worry about other women?'

'If I did, I'd have to worry about Davina, wouldn't I?' retorted Sara lightly, then added more seriously, 'Thank you for your concern and your advice, Ida. I'd like to live with Janos all the time, but I also like the work I do. I really must hurry now, or I'll miss the train.'

'I wish you'd miss the train for once,' Janos growled in her ear as they leaned against one another in the back of a taxi on the way to the station. 'But always you must rush away, back to Tom Caldwell.'

'Not back to Tom, silly,' she scolded softly, touching his cheek. 'Back to my job.'

'Which means more to you than I do,' he accused, rubbing his nose against hers. 'Caldwell cracks the whip and you run to obey. You never obey me.'

'Oh, surely you're not jealous of Tom?' she protested with a laugh, secretly delighted that he could feel jealous. 'You have no need to be. His relationship with me is strictly that of the head of the design department to the most junior of the designers. It's something like your relationship to Davina Williams. You're the teacher and she's the pupil.'

'Who told you she's taking lessons from me?'

'Ida did.'

'And doesn't it make you feel jealous?' he challenged.

'Should it?'

'Perhaps.'

'Janos!' she exclaimed, pushing away from him. 'You're twenty-nine, nearly thirteen years older than she is, and she's still at school. Surely you don't encourage her to ... to ...' She was too shocked to put into words what she imagined might happen during Davina's lessons with him.

'I don't have to encourage her. She's both precocious and promiscuous. In fact she's a damned nuisance.' His voice grated oddly and he turned to her suddenly. Against her neck his hand moved with a savage urgency round to her nape. 'Kiss me, Sara,' he whispered. 'And stay another night with me. Stay two or three or four nights, the whole week in fact, right up to the time we leave for the States for that tour. I'll be away nearly two months, so stay with me. We owe ourselves some time together.'

She lifted her mouth to his and for a few moments the darkness whirled about her.

'All right, I'll stay,' she whispered, when he raised his head. 'I'll stay with you until you leave for the States.'

CHAPTER FOUR

THE clapping and the cheers broke out spontaneously as the concerto came to an end on a note of hope, and there was a rustle of clothing as people sprang to their feet in a standing ovation. Jolted back into the present, Sara also stood up and clapped, watching Janos bow, shake hands with the conductor and then the leader of the orchestra, wave to the other musicians and then turn back again to bow to the audience before leaving the stage, the conductor behind him.

But the applause didn't stop and the audience did not sit down. Back Janos came, alone this time, smiling and obviously delighted with the applause. Again he shook hands with the leader. Again he waved his arm to the other musicians in an attempt to persuade them to rise to their feet and share the ovation with him. But they remained in their seats, clapping with the audience.

He left the stage again and the shouts of 'Encore' began and were repeated over and over again to the accompaniment of regular hand-clapping. After a while the conductor appeared, leading Janos back on to the stage. He tapped with his baton on the rail at the back of his podium and the clapping subsided as the audience sat down again. Janos moved forward.

'In appreciation of the gratifying welcome you have given me tonight I would like to play for you as an encore, Sérénade Mélancolique by Tchaikovsky,' he announced, and once again it seemed to Sara that he looked right at her.

Oh God, she couldn't stand it, she thought. She couldn't bear to sit there and listen to that hauntingly beautiful music. She would have to leave. But it was too late. The orchestra had started to play and Janos was lifting his violin. With his eyes closed as he concentrated on remembering the notes he began to play the first solo melody, and immediately Sara was transported back to the flat in Chelsea, with its view of the River Thames and the days she had spent there with him before he had left to go on tour with the New Century Orchestra. He had practised this piece every day she had been there in preparation for a recording he was to make of it and she had come to know it intimately, had found in it an expression of her own feelings regarding him, loving and passionate yet sad, because deep down inside she had always known, as Tom had predicted, that she would never come first with Janos. No woman would. No man or child either. Always music would come first with him. He had dedicated his life to it.

During that week she stayed with him in London there were moments, however, when she was able to believe that perhaps she did mean more to him than any other person in his life; when she experienced brief flashes of ecstatic joy, a union of body and mind with his body and mind. But once he had gone away and she returned to Manchester she felt bereft, as if he had left her for ever and would never return. The only way she was able to cope with such emotional devastation was to immerse herself completely in her work and deliberately blot all thoughts of him from her mind, as she guessed he deliberately blotted her from his memory. It was the only way she could survive without him.

The eight weeks he was away passed slowly. Spring came early that year. There was no snow and crocuses, yellow purple and orange, sprinkled parks and gardens with bright colour, followed by daffodils, pale narcissi and vivid tulips. The day Sara arrived in London to be at Janos's flat when he returned the next day from the States the temperature reached a record high for April, and the rooms were filled with sunshine as she busied herself cleaning and cooking in preparation for his coming.

In the evening she went to the Williamses' house, invited there by Ida who had a guest from Austria staying with her, a singer called Elisabeth Herrenkoff. When Ida introduced Sara to Elisabeth she said,

'Sara is married to Janos Vaszary, who is now leader of the orchestra Gareth conducts. I believe you know Janos quite well.'

'Of course I do.' About thirty-five years of age, Elisabeth was pretty and fair-haired. She spoke English perfectly with only the slightest of accents. 'He stayed with my husband and me in Vienna after he left Hungary. It was I who first introduced him to Gareth.'

'Then you must be the friend with whom he left his precious violin,' Sara said with a smile.

'That is right.' Elisabeth's vivid blue eyes twinkled with amusement. 'And you must be the English girl he met in Salzburg, who promised to marry him if he ever reached this country. You play the flute, do you not?'

Surprise held Sara silent for a few seconds. What should she say? How could she lie with Ida and Davina both there watching and listening with interest and knowing she didn't play the flute?

'No, that was my cousin Cecilia,' she said quietly. 'She was in Salzburg the summer before last, but by the time Janos came here she was married. She now lives in California.'

'So Janos married you instead.' The blue eyes were suddenly very shrewd, but in a kindly way, and stepping forward Elisabeth put her hands on Sara's shoulders and kissed her on both cheeks. 'I'm glad he did,' she smiled. 'And I hope you are very happy together.'

The awkward moment was over, but for Sara the evening was spoilt, although she tried very hard not to show that Elisabeth's mention of Cecilia's promise to marry Janos had disturbed her.

'It is wonderful to hear that Janos is becoming a success here,' Elisabeth said when she and Sara were alone for a short time while Ida was in the kitchen making coffee for them and Davina had disappeared, probably to her room to practise the violin. 'I expect he has told you how difficult life was for him in Hungary.'

'He has told me a little. He doesn't seem to want to talk about it, although sometimes I know he broods about the past.'

'I'm not surprised he doesn't want to talk about it,' said the forthright Elisabeth with a graceful little shudder. 'He suffered greatly. Twice he was in prison.'

'Why?' Sara exclaimed, her eyes widening.

'For attempting to leave the country without permission. The last time was just before he escaped. You can imagine what imprisonment was like for someone of his exuberance, his love of life and music. And the first time he lost Eva and their child.' Elisabeth broke off and shook her head sadly. 'A weaker person would have given up all hope,' she added. 'But not Janos. His faith in himself, his knowledge that he has been blessed with a great gift, the ability to bring pleasure to thousands of people through playing the world's finest music, has helped him to keep going and to surmount all obstacles.'

'Who . . . who was Eva?' Sara asked, her voice a little strained.

'His mistress,' replied Elisabeth. 'I cannot call her his wife because they were not married. But they lived together in Budapest as if they were and he was extremely fond of her. She died in childbirth, and the baby died some hours later. Didn't he tell you about her?'

Sara shook her head dumbly. Ida came into the room with a tray and the course of conversation changed. Sara didn't stay much longer, using as an excuse to leave the desire to go to bed early because she wanted to be up and about early next morning before Janos arrived from the airport.

She went upstairs alone to get her coat from the Williamses' bedroom where she had left it as usual, and was putting it on when Davina sidled into the room.

'How does it feel to know that Janos married you instead of your cousin when he found out she was married to someone else?' asked the girl. 'What's it like to find out you were only a substitute for her?'

Sara pretended she was more interested in buckling the belt of her coat than she was in the sneering remarks. It seemed that Davina wasn't such a naïve schoolgirl as she had believed. She was a dangerously attractive young woman who had no hesitation in using her sensual charms and had used them on Janos already.

'What makes you think I'm a substitute?' Sara queried as lightly as she could.

'Oh, I'm very good at putting two and two together. I heard what Elisabeth said about your cousin promising to marry Janos if he came to this country. And I know marriage to a British citizen was one way he could be accepted as an immigrant.'

'How do you know?' Sara demanded sharply.

'I overheard him and Daddy talking last year. Daddy asked him if he knew of anyone he could marry and he said that he knew a woman in the north, so Daddy told him to go and get married and he'd arrange for him to play with the orchestra. Janos went north intending to marry your cousin, but had to marry you instead. That makes you second fiddle to her. He didn't marry you because he loves you but because he had to marry someone quickly. He doesn't love you.' Davina's bold heavy-lidded glance swept over Sara. 'In fact I don't believe anyone as hot-blooded as Janos could fall for a cold fish like you.'

Pulling on her gloves, Sara struggled hard to control an urge to slap Davina's gloating face. She picked up her handbag, slid it under her arm and walked towards the door. When she was on a level with Davina she smiled at her.

'You are in a bad way, aren't you?' she said sweetly. 'What's the matter? Did Janos turn you down? Are you hurt because he regards you as a mere child and not a woman, a pest he could manage very well without? Are you striking out at me because you're jealous of me? Because you know I've had something from Janos you will never have?'

'He doesn't love you, I know he doesn't. He loves only music!' Davina hissed, but her face crumpled as if she were going to burst into tears. 'He won't stay with you for ever, you'll see. He'll leave you one day because he won't need you any more. You'll have served his purpose . . .'

Sara didn't wait to hear any more. Pulling the door open, she left the room and hurried downstairs to say goodbye to Ida and Elisabeth.

He doesn't love you, I know he doesn't. He'll leave you one day. You'll have served his purpose! All night Davina's words tormented her, rousing to the surface of her mind the suspicion that had been buried there; the suspicion that Tom had planted in her mind, and as if to back up everything Davina had said Tom's words came storming into her memory to add to the torment. *You fool! You blithering idiot! You've been conned.* And as the night went by slowly and heavily she began to see quite clearly that she had been taken in by an old trick. Secretly longing to be loved, she had fallen for the first man who had come along and had seemed to share her dream of romance.

But now she could bury her head in the sand no longer. Over a year ago Janos had asked her not to lie because he didn't want lies to spoil their friendship, and she had agreed that any future relationship between them had to be based on complete frankness. Only in that way could they learn to trust each other. Now it seemed to her that all his behaviour had been a lie. He had needed a marriage certificate, so he had seduced her with loving words, and she had played into his hands willingly, blindly.

Dawn was breaking when she fell asleep at last, dry-eyed, having been too disgusted by her own stupidity to weep, and she didn't wake early as she had intended, so that the first she knew of Janos's arrival was the pressure of his lips against hers and the swelling and tautening of her breasts to the urgent caress of his fingers.

'Oh, you're back,' she whispered sleepily, forgetful in those first moments of wakefulness of what she had learned about him the previous day. Joyfully her arms went around him in welcome. He was undressed, his skin slightly damp from bathing, and was in bed beside her, desire throbbing through every part of him and he gathered her against him to smother her mouth with his in one of his paradoxical kisses, the violence of passion overlaid with sweet seductive tenderness.

'No, not yet.' The memory of the night's torment was suddenly upon her, revulsion of feeling lending her strength so that she was able to push him away and slide from beneath his. 'Not now. Not now.'

His hand was in her hair, winding in it as if he intended to haul her back and have his way with her without her consent, and she felt her scalp tingle painfully. Then she was free and slipping over the edge of the bed to the floor.

'Why not now?' whispered Janos, coming after her and crouching beside her on the floor. 'Eight weeks is a long time for me to be without you or for you to be without me.' He encircled her with his arms again and she felt she was going to drown in the hot tide of his uncontrolled passion. Fighting for breath, wrenching her mouth from his, she pushed him away again and jumped to her feet.

'No, no! I don't want to. I don't want you—not now. Please don't touch me any more. We must talk first. I'll make some coffee . . .' Her breath caught in her throat as Janos stood up and advanced upon her, and with a little moan of distress she turned and ran from the room.

In the kitchen she filled the kettle, her hands shaking as she held it beneath the tap. It was the first time since they had married that she had ever rejected his amorous advances, and the effort involved was making her feel physically ill. She was afraid too of how he might react. Even after a year of being married to him she sensed there were depths to Janos she had not yet plumbed and that possibly he had a capacity for violence handed down to him from barbarian ancestors.

'Sara!' His voice, sharply cold, spoke behind her, and she turned to face him after plugging in the kettle. Dressed only in a karate-style robe with wide sleeves and a tie belt, he stood in the doorway, staring at her from under frowning eyebrows. His eyes held a dangerous glitter and the set of his mouth warned her that his temper was simmering. 'What is wrong?' he demanded. 'Why are you . . . like this?' As if words failed him he made a gesture with one hand. It seemed to her that his hand swept in a denigrating fashion up from her feet to her tangled hair, criticising her appearance. He was finding her lacking in something he wanted and so he was putting her down.

'I'm tired. I didn't sleep very well,' she replied.

'Because your conscience was pricking you, perhaps?' he sneered.

'I beg your pardon?' she gasped, her head going up with offended pride. 'Why should *my* conscience prick *me*?'

'As I have said, eight weeks is a long time, for both of us, for you as well as for me. You could have become tired of waiting for my return and found comfort with some other man.' He shrugged and coming into the room, sat on the corner of the table, thrusting his hands in the pockets of his robe as he continued to stare at her.

'That is . . . is . . . a terrible thing to say to me,' she whispered, utterly astounded that he should distrust her so much. 'How could you even think it?'

'It isn't hard to think it,' he retorted: 'Just now you refused to make love with me. Naturally I search for reasons. The obvious one that comes to mind is that you have found another lover. Have you?' His voice was menacing.

'Supposing I have?' she flung back at him, her own temper rising now. 'What would you do?'

For a moment he studied her face, his eyes hard and cold assessing her. The kettle boiled and he slid off the table to go and unplug it.

'Next time I go away I do not come back to you,' he said flatly.

'I see. So you wouldn't like playing second fiddle to another man,' she taunted. 'Is that why you wouldn't come back?'

'Yes.' Janos turned and came over to her, the expression in his eyes changing, his mouth tilting in its attractive smile. 'You should know me by now. I have to be the first in anything, in love as well as in music.' His hands curved about her waist, their heat burning through the thin stuff of her nightgown. His head bent, his lips aiming towards her throat, but before they could ravish it she moved away, reaching into the cupboard for mugs and instant coffee.

'I met a friend of yours yesterday,' she said, her voice cool and unshaken as she spooned coffee into the mugs. 'At the Williamses' house. Her name is Elisabeth Herrenhoff.'

'Elisabeth is in London?' he exclaimed. 'How long does she stay? I hope I will see her before she leaves. Did she tell you I lived with her and her husband in Vienna while I was waiting to come here?'

'She told me many things about you that I didn't know before—about how you were imprisoned; about Eva and the baby. Janos, why have you never told me about Eva?'

He gave her that strangely blank stare as if he were trying to penetrate into her mind and find out what lay behind her question.

'Why should I tell you about someone I knew years ago and who is no longer alive?' he said stiffly.

'Did you love her?'

'Ah, so that is your problem. You are jealous of her,' he mocked. 'I loved her in my fashion,' he added, shrugging slightly. Then his glance fell away from hers, a muscle twitched at the corner of his mouth and bone gleamed along the angle of his jaw. 'I try hard not to remember her,' he added in a low voice. 'For a while we lived together. Then I was put in prison, and while I was there she gave birth to the baby. She died because I was not there to take care of her properly.' He swung away from her and went to look out of the window. 'You understand now why I did not tell you about her? There are some things I prefer not to talk about.'

'Is Cecilia's promise to marry you if you came to this country one of them?' asked Sara.

Janos whirled round to face her, his forehead creasing in a frown of puzzlement.

'No,' he said.

'Then why didn't you ever tell me about it?'

'I thought you knew,' he said slowly, coming back across the room towards her. 'I believed she must have told you when you talked to her on the phone that night I came to Manchester.'

'She didn't tell me. I didn't know . . . until yesterday.'

'Elisabeth said something?'

'She assumed I was the English girl you had met in Salzburg who promised to marry you if you ever came to this country and who played the flute. Did you ask Cecilia to marry you? And did she say she would?'

'Yes.' He spoke curtly, watching her with suddenly wary eyes.

'I suppose that was the way you hoped to be able to stay in this country,' she commented. 'Marriage to a British girl would make it possible for you to stay.'

'I cannot deny that was the plan,' he replied in a low voice.

'Then it must have been a great blow to you when you found out she hadn't kept her promise but had married someone else,' she accused.

'By then I had met you,' he said quietly, stepping towards her again. Sara stepped back quickly.

'And I was the substitute for Cecilia,' she cried, hurt getting the better of her. 'Oh, Tom warned me. He said you'd duped me into marrying you. He said you'd turned on the charm and it had worked. My God, how it worked!' Her voice quavered and broke at last. She would have run from the room to hide in the bathroom until she had controlled her emotions, but Janos reached out and caught hold of her shoulders. 'Let go of me!' she flung at him, trying to twist free and failing.

'Not until you have listened to me,' he said tautly. 'It is true I asked Cecilia to marry me and she agreed to . . . if I could get to this country. I came. I met you and I fell in love with you. Oh, yes I did, Sara,' he added sharply when she shook her head, her face showing her disbelief. 'Far from being a blow to me when you told me Cecilia was married it was a great relief, because all the time on that journey to Stonethwaite I was wondering how I could get out of marrying her.' Seeing her mouth twist with scepticism, he gave her a little shake. 'Don't you believe me?'

'No. No—oh, I don't know what to believe. I'm all mixed up,' Sara moaned.

He let go of her, his hands returning to the pockets of his robe, his eyes going blank and his mouth growing taut.

'You prefer to believe Tom, of course.' Bitterness grated in his voice. 'It is only natural. You have known him longer than you have known me. He's a fellow countryman of yours, while I'm the stranger, the suspicious foreigner who will go to any lengths to get what he wants.' He paused, then added heaviily, 'What I have told you is true. I have no further defence to make. I thought you understood how I feel about you.'

'I don't believe you fell in love with me when you say you did,' she accused shakily. 'Oh, you made a good pretence of falling in love. You're a very practised lover, too practised, I can see that now. No doubt you'd had lots of experience.' She broke off, biting her lip. 'But you don't love anyone except yourself,' she went on. 'You didn't love Eva, you didn't love Cecilia and you don't love me. I realise you're a gifted musician, but . . . but as a person you . . . you're despicable, and I . . . I . . . never want to see you again. Never!'

She turned and rushed from the room before the tears could run over from her eyes on to her cheeks. Going into the bathroom, she turned on

the bath taps so that the sound of water would
drown the sound of her sobbing. When she had
washed and was in more control of herself she
went through to the bedroom and after dressing
began to pack her case in readiness to leave. She
was just fastening the case when Janos came
into the room. Fully dressed now in sleek black
pants and a white shirt over which he wore a black
velour sweater, he stood in the middle of the
room, his arms crossed over his chest, his face
hard and expressionless as if carved from rock.

'Where are you going?' he asked at last.

'To Manchester, on the next train.'

'Back to Tom?' he asked jeeringly, his mouth
twisting.

'Yes, back to Tom,' she retorted, stung by his
jeer. 'At least he doesn't pretend or take advantage
of a situation like you do. At least I know where I
stand with him. He would never deliberately trick
me as you've done.'

'Sara——' he began, and stopped to rake a hand
through his hair, his face losing its rock-hardness
as he frowned with the effort to find words. 'I
realise it must look to you as if I tricked you because I had to do everything in such a hurry. I
thought you knew about Cecilia and me and I
believed that what had happened to me had
happened to you too. I believed that in spite of
your efforts to deceive me and prevent me from
seeing Cecilia you liked me, were in love with me
just a little bit.' He came towards her again, his
hands reaching out to her. 'Surely you won't deny

that we have loved each other during the past year,' he said softly.

'Stay away from me!' Sara said sharply, backing off. 'Don't you dare try to . . . to . . . seduce me again with your lover's words and hands!'

Janos stopped in mid-stride and thrust his hands into his pockets. His face was very pale, the lines of weariness caused by the night flight across the Atlantic showing up very clearly around his eyes.

'I have to remind you that you are my wife and I have a right to be with you, to touch you,' he said quietly.

'You don't have that right any more,' she retorted, 'because I'm taking it away from you. You used marriage to me for your own advantage. You would still use it for your own advantage if I let you, and for that I can never forgive you!' She picked up the jacket of her tweed suit and pulled it on. 'So don't bother to turn on the charm hoping to persuade me to stay with you. I'm leaving as soon as I can get a taxi and I won't be coming back. Excuse me.'

She walked past him into the living room and went straight to the phone to dial the taxi service. By the time she had finished ordering the taxi Janos, wearing a suede golf jacket over his sweater as if he intended to go out, was coming into the room carrying her case. He set the case down by the front door and turned back to look at her.

'You're not going to attempt to come with me?' she queried cautiously, and he shook his head.

'No, I'm not coming with you and I won't follow you. You need time to get over this upset, so I'm going to give you time,' he said coolly.

'You . . . you agree to a separation, then?' she whispered.

'If that is what you want,' he replied. 'I am going back to the States next month and I will be there for several months, maybe even longer.'

'Why?' Sara was surprised and all she could think of was what Davina had said. *He'll leave you one day, you'll see. You'll have served your purpose.* Now it seemed as if the girl had known more about him than she had. Perhaps he had told Davina during one of the violin lessons! Bitterness welled up in her, souring her attitude towards him and making her hate him for his duplicity.

'While I was in New York with the orchestra, Miklos Zala, the great conductor who left Hungary after the second world war, heard me play. He has invited me to play as soloist in a concert he is conducting next month at the Lincoln Center. It is something I have always dreamed of, an opportunity I cannot afford to miss. Afterwards, if I am lucky, there will be other engagements to play with other great orchestras and conductors over there.'

'But will you be able to stay in the States?' she asked. The ice which she had once thought he had melted for ever was creeping back along her veins as she realised he was not going to put his relationship with her first as she had hoped he would when he knew it was in danger of breaking up. 'Or will you have to marry an American woman before you can live there?' she added tauntingly. 'Please let me know if you do and I'll arrange to divorce you.'

Across the room Janos's eyes blazed into hers. He muttered something savage in Hungarian and was coming towards her, a threat in every stride, when the bell rang. The taxi had arrived. Snatching up her case, Sara opened the door and hurried through it, slamming it in Janos's face. She half expected and perhaps half hoped for it to be wrenched open and for him to come after her. But the door stayed closed. He didn't follow her and, as she went down to the ground floor, she acknowledged drearily that he never would.

Leaving him, cutting herself off from all contact with him was not easy for her, and after a while she began to wonder if she was punishing herself much more severely than she was punishing him as she ached to see him, and to hear his voice. Three weeks went by and she was thinking of getting in touch with Ida Williams to ask for news of Janos when she received a letter from him It was very short.

'Tomorrow I go to New York,' he had written. 'It is arranged that I live there for a while. I would have liked to have come to Manchester to see you before leaving this country, but I know you do not want to see me again—*ever*, so I do not come. I would like to write more, to tell you what being with you during the past twelve months has meant to me, but I cannot write English well. The spelling defeats me. Also, what is the use? You would not believe me. Janos.'

There were many crossings out in the letter as if he had indeed had difficulty in writing it, and Sara sat and stared at it a long time, wanting to cry with regret for the dream they had shared and which was now shattered.

She did not reply to the letter, not having any address in New York, and he did not write to her again. As time went by their marriage began to seem like a fantasy, a brief bubble of romance which had burst as soon as it had encountered sharp reality. Separated not only physically with thousands of miles of ocean between them but also spiritually as they both pursued their careers, Sara began to feel as if they had never met.

But she did hear about him occasionally, mostly from Ida Williams, who wrote to her regularly, often enclosing cuttings from music magazines and from newspapers in which Janos was mentioned. Slowly but surely he was climbing the ladder of success as he performed and recorded with some of the world's great orchestras and conductors, and there was a certain similarity in the remarks made by the critics about his playing. 'Vaszary is one of the foremost violinists of the day,' wrote one. 'Let us be thankful that he has been allowed to come to this country to enchant us,' wrote another. 'He possesses a radiant tone and an indefinable, indescribable sense of beauty,' raved another. 'He's a magician with technique to

burn, but was there ever a more "human" violinist, one more capable of communicating his
feelings about the music to the man in the street?'
enthused another.

It was when she read such reviews that Sara
felt a certain pride because she had known Janos.
Then she would remember how he had tricked
her and she would deliberately squash all
memories of him, hiding the cuttings away at the
back of a drawer with his letter. One day when
they had been separated long enough she would
file for a divorce, unless he divorced her first.

Life went on. Burying herself in her work in
order to forget the fiasco of her marriage, she was
successful too, and when Tom Caldwell was
promoted to a senior managerial position in the
textile company Sara stepped into the position he
had held as manager of the design department.

It was at Christmas time in the second year of
her separation from Janos that she received an
invitation from Cecilia's parents to spend the
short holiday at Stonethwaite. They were expecting Cecilia and her husband and their infant
grandson to stay for the festive season and were
sure she would like to see Cecilia again.

'In fact, I wrote to Mummy and told her to
invite you,' Cecilia said on Christmas Eve when
Sara arrived. They were both in Sara's bedroom
where she was unpacking the presents she had
brought and was hanging her clothes in the wardrobe. 'I want to know what's happened between
you and Janos,' Cecilia went on as she lolled

gracefully on the bed. 'You must know, of course, that he's hit the jackpot in the States. He receives fantastic reviews in all the top American papers and music journals for his performances, both live and on records.'

'Have you been to hear him in concert?' asked Sara.

'No, not yet. But I will as soon as he comes to either L.A. or 'Frisco, and I'm collecting his records. What happened, Sara? Why aren't you with him over there? You are still married to him, aren't you?'

'Yes, but we decided to separate,' Sara replied coolly.

She glanced sideways at her cousin. Cecilia hadn't changed much over the years. Although she was the mother of the healthy, lusty boy of eighteen months who was sleeping in the next room she still looked very youthful with her golden hair hanging about her oval face and her clear grey eyes seeming to shine with innocence or to twinkle with mischief, depending on her mood. 'Did you really promise to marry Janos when you met him in Salzburg?' Sara asked quickly before she could change her mind.

'Yes, I did.' Cecilia's lips curved in a slightly rueful grin. 'Naughty of me, wasn't it? But you must know by now that he's very difficult to refuse when he turns on the charm. He told me it was one way he could stay in England if he ever managed to get here. He said it would be a marriage of convenience, nothing else, until he'd established himself here with an orchestra. I was rather infatuated with him at the time, so I said yes. I didn't believe for one moment that he would come and I was really in a panic that night you phoned and told me he'd arrived. It was impossible to tell you why I didn't want him to come to Stonethwaite with Mother and Dad there, listening to everything I was saying.'

'You can tell me now,' said Sara pointedly.

'Well, put yourself in my shoes. If you'd been about to marry Philip would you have wanted a refugee from another country turning up and telling your husband-to-be that you'd promised to marry him first?' exclaimed Cecilia. 'Philip is a darling and I love him very much, but he's a bit puritanical and he wouldn't have approved what I'd done—and I couldn't risk offending him, just then, when we were going to be married the next day, could I?'

'No, I suppose you couldn't,' agreed Sara with a sigh. 'But I can't help wishing you'd told me you'd promised to marry Janos.'

'I assumed he would tell you. He did, didn't he?'

'No. Someone else did, later. He assumed that you'd told me.'

'I knew I could depend on you to help me out,' Cecilia went on, laughter bubbling in her voice. 'But I have to admit I didn't expect you to go all the way and substitute for me. But it turned out all right in the end, didn't it?'

'Did it? What do you mean?' asked Sara, turning away from the wardrobe to stare at her.

'Well, he's been able to do what he couldn't do in Hungary and he's a great success, thanks to both of us. Don't you feel glad you were able to help him?' Cecilia broke off, her eyes widening as she stared at Sara. 'Oh, my God,' she groaned. 'Don't tell me you fell in love with him?' she whispered.

'Yes, I did. Foolish of me, wasn't it?' said Sara with a crooked smile.

'I don't know,' said Cecilia slowly. 'It would depend on whether he fell in love with you at the same time. Did he?'

'He said he did, but I think he was only pretending so that I would agree to marry him when he found out you were married to Philip. I know now that he was told to hurry up and get married so he could join the New Century Orchestra.'

'My God!' breathed Cecilia again, her eyes still very wide. 'How long since you separated?'

'It will be two years next April. I told him I didn't want to see him again and he went away, to the States. We don't keep in touch and next year we'll probably get a divorce.' Sara forced a smile. 'It's all over now. I made a mistake and I've paid the penalty. It won't happen again.'

'I'm sorry, love,' said Cecilia in a subdued voice. 'I thought . . . well, I believed you were tougher, I suppose. I mean, you were never like me, falling in and out of love all the time, and I suppose I assumed you'd be able to cope with someone like Janos.'

'I'd rather not talk about it any more,' Sara said in a stifled voice.

'Okay, we won't,' said Cecilia, cheerful again as she rolled off the bed. 'We'll talk about you. Tell me what you're doing now. Mum says you're a real career woman. Do you still have Tom Caldwell for a boss?'

'No. He was promoted and I'm the boss of the design department now.'

'Good for you! What does that involve? Any chances of travelling?'

'As a matter of fact I'll be going to Georgia in the spring some time, to visit some cotton mills there. Ferris Fabrics have an association with a company in West Georgia which makes sheets, towels and curtain materials.'

'Oh, great,' said Cecilia excitedly. 'You can come and see us afterwards. Take your vacation. We live in a simply super house overlooking the Pacific, just south of Big Sur, and I'm into all the local activities. I actually play in the woodwind section of the local symphony orchestra. It's a non-profit-making organisation formed by local residents to promote and encourage the performance of orchestral music. When would you be in Georgia, do you think?'

'Probably towards the end of April.'

'Then you could be with us for the last concert of the season. Oh, please come, Sara, even if you don't have to go to Georgia. California is a fabulous place and you'd have a wonderful time.'

And so it had been planned last Christmas and Sara had come, arriving over two weeks ago, and as Cecilia had predicted she had had a wonderful time. She had been made welcome by Cecilia's in-laws and friends in a way she had never been welcomed anywhere before, and tonight the crazy little hope which so often jiggled up and down at the back of her mind had been fulfilled. She had seen Janos again, had heard him playing and had discovered that, given time, she had forgiven him and was ready to fall in love with him again.

No. No! The words screeched through her mind and she opened her eyes quickly, afraid that she might have shouted out loud, and she looked straight at Janos. Again she had the impression that he was looking at her and was playing the Serenade only for her.

That was it, he was trying to hypnotise her as he had so many times with the warmth and depth of his playing. He was trying to trick her into believing that he knew what it was like to love passionately and to regret the passing of such love from his life. She must remember that he was an artist, first and foremost, a clever creator of illusion through music, and that was all. He didn't really feel deeply about anyone. He loved only himself and music.

The last sad notes of the Sérénade were played. There was a moment of complete silence. Then Janos lowered his bow and the applause broke out, filling the auditorium with waves of sound as everyone sprang to their feet again.

CHAPTER FIVE

'THAT was wonderful, simply wonderful!' said Myrna Bixman breathlessly as she and Sara made their way up the aisle between the seats towards the exit of the auditorium. 'Didn't you think so?'

'Yes. Yes, I did,' replied Sara vaguely. She was still feeling bemused by memories and was slightly disorientated, not sure whether she was in California or England.

'And it's such an honour for our little county orchestra to have him play with them,' Myrna continued as they stepped out into the foyer of the small university theatre and were followed by Philip, Glenn and Charles. 'And it's all thanks to dear Cecilia that he agreed to come.'

'Oh?' Sara was startled back into reality. 'She didn't tell me.'

'I expect she wanted to surprise you,' said Myrna with a sort of ironic innocence, because she couldn't possibly know what a surprise Janos's appearance had been for Sara. Unless Cecilia had told everyone he was her cousin's estranged husband. Sara stared at Myrna's heavily tanned face, wondering how much the woman knew about her.

'How did she get in touch with Mr Vaszary?' she asked.

'She found out that he was performing in L. A. earlier this week, so she went to see him,' replied Myrna, using her superior height to look around the crowd of people now milling about the foyer. 'You'll know, of course, that she met him once when she was a student. Luckily he remembered her and agreed to come and play to us. I'm hoping she'll bring him out here to meet us and that I'll be able to persuade him to come to the party Charles and I are giving for all the orchestra and members of the Guild. You'll come too, my dear? I'm sure Glenn will be happy to drive you to the ranch.'

'Yes. Thank you,' Sara answered, wondering in sudden panic how she could get away before Cecilia appeared with Janos.

'There's Cecilia now!' exclaimed Myrna gleefully, her face beaming. 'And she has Vaszary with her. I expect she's looking for us.' She waved a bare thick arm above the heads of the people crowding about them.

Standing on tiptoe, really wanting to see him, she told herself, but curious to know if he had changed, Sara looked in the direction Myrna had waved. Against the black of Janos's tailcoat Cecilia's golden hair shone like a beacon and she was smiling a smile of smug satisfaction as she introduced him to various people on her way through the crowd. Behind Janos came another woman. Fairly tall, with an elegantly slim figure shown off in a slinky black dress which glittered with sequins and was far too extravagant in style for the occasion, she had smooth black hair and her strong, classically-shaped features seemed vaguely familiar. She was also smiling as she acknowledged the greetings of various people.

'Magda Scott,' Glenn spoke quietly, close to Sara and she turned towards him. 'The woman behind Vaszary,' he explained in answer to her look of enquiry. 'She's a film actress—originally from Hungary too. Scott is the last name of her first husband. Rumour has it that she and Vaszary are having an affair and that as soon as she's divorced her second husband he's going to marry her.'

'But he can't marry her,' Sara blurted. 'He's married already.'

'Is he? To whom? It can't be common knowledge that he is or it would have been mentioned in that write-up about him in the programme.'

Sara bit down hard on her lower lip as she watched Janos bending gallantly over the hand of one of the more elderly members of the Symphony Orchestra's Ladies' Guild.

'I'm sure I read somewhere that he's married,' she said.

'Well, maybe he's going to get unmarried—like Magda is,' drawled Glenn. 'It happens all the time with the Hollywood set.'

'But Janos doesn't belong to the Hollywood set,' Sara said hotly. 'He's . . .' She became aware that Glenn was staring at her, his fair eyebrows raised in surprise. 'He's not like that,' she finished lamely.

'Sounds as if you know him,' he commented.

'I do,' she began, and was interrupted by Cecilia's laughing voice.

'Sara, oh, Sara love, look round and see who I've brought to see you!'

I never want to see you again. Never. Her own words echoed mockingly through her head as Sara slowly turned her head up, her face composed although her hands were clenched tightly at her sides, hidden from view by the folds of the full-skirted summer dress she was wearing and her heart felt as if it would burst at any minute.

'Sara, you remember Janos, don't you?' said Cecilia. Was she being deliberately cruel? Or was she putting on an act for the benefit of the watchers and listeners?

'Of course I do!' Sara kept her cool and was pleased with the sound of her voice. She held out a hand. 'How are you?' she asked politely. 'You played beautifully tonight.'

The black-rimmed tawny eyes glinted mockingly at her and the chiselled lips curved into an elusive smile as he took her hand in his. Then he bowed and raised her hand to his lips. It took all her self-control not to pull her hand free.

'I played for you,' he said softly as he straightened up. Keeping hold of her hand, he looked right into her eyes, his own sombre now. Haunted by memories? It would be easy to think so.

'You knew I was here?' she exclaimed in a whisper, completely unaware now of anyone else who might be watching or listening. Once again she was trapped in the fragile web of their relationship, and it was as if the two years of their separation had never been.

'Cecilia told me just before the concert began,' Janos told her, and looked right into her eyes again as if he were trying to convey to her that she meant more to him than any other person in the world.

Distrustful of that look, Sara glanced away from him and slid her fingers free of his hand. She was convinced he was doing what he had always done, what he couldn't help doing when he met a woman who attracted him. He was pretending. No one in the immediate vicinity seemed to be watching them after all, because Cecilia had drawn the attention of Myrna, Charles and Glenn to herself and Philip was with another group of people.

'Sara, if it's possible I would like to meet with you somewhere,' Janos was saying quietly when he was interrupted.

'Janos.' The woman's voice was deep and throaty and she had just the suspicion of an attractive accent, enough to fascinate. 'Do we have to stay here? Can't we go back to Beverly Hills?'

'Not yet.' He turned back to Sara and a sort of malicious mischief glimmered in his eyes. 'Sara, I'd like you to meet Magda Scott. Magda, this is Sara, my wife.'

He was like a boy who had set off a firework deliberately as he stood there, hands in his pockets, laughing silently at the surprise on

Magda's face, thought Sara. But he had surprised her too and she looked round quickly, wondering if anyone else had heard.

'But you must be kidding!' Magda had recovered her poise and her laughter sounded quite genuine as her glance swept contemptuously over Sara so that she felt dowdy in her printed cotton dress.

'No, I am not kidding,' said Janos serenely. 'Sara and I have been married for three years.'

'Mr Vaszary,' Myrna was on his other side, at her most persuasive. 'We would really be delighted if you would stay and hear the rest of the concert and then come to the party my husband and I are giving at our home afterwards.'

'Excuse me,' Sara muttered, and turning away, pushed through the people who were converging on the doors of the auditorium to return to their seats now that the intermission was over.

'Hey, you're going the wrong way!' Glenn was at her side, a hand on his arm.

'I can't go back in there,' she said in a low voice. 'I can't bear it any more. I must get away.' She pressed a hand against her forehead.

'Mmm, you do look kind of pale,' he agreed. 'I guess it's a bit stuffy in here tonight. How about some fresh air?'

With a hand under her arm he guided her towards the exit of the building and they stepped out into the velvety darkness of the Californian night. The scents of many flowers and shrubs

filled the air and crickets sang in the under-
growth.

'Feeling okay now?' asked Glenn.

'Yes, thank you. I think you were right and lack
of air was the problem.'

'Do you want to go back?'

'No, not really.'

'Then would you like me to drive you somewhere? Back to Phil's house? Or would you consider taking a ride along the coast to Big Sur, to
my hideaway up there? I've been wanting to take
you there for some time, but the opportunity has
never presented itself. We could have a drink and
listen to a different kind of music.'

'But what about the party Myrna is giving for
the orchestra?'

'Do you want to go to it?'

Sara had a sudden vision of Magda Scott, her
red-tipped fingers sliding possessively into the
crook of Janos's arm and felt jealousy flare up
within her. Supposing Janos accepted Myrna's
invitation and took Magda to the party with him
how would she be able to keep cool and calm in
the face of such provocation? She wouldn't. She
would want to scratch the woman's eyes out.

'No, I don't want to go,' she said, smiling up at
Glenn. 'I'd much rather see your hideaway and
listen to a different sort of music.'

'Then what are we waiting for?' he drawled,
taking hold of her arm again and urging her towards the rows of cars in the parking lot. 'Let's
go now.'

An hour's drive through the star-spangled
darkness, the big car purring contentedly as it ate
up the miles of a road that roller-coasted northwards, sometimes hanging dizzily on the edge of
cliffs above the sea that smashed in light-reflect-
ing foam against rugged rocks. Then at last Glenn
was turning the car off the road under windswept
Monterey pines to drive along a narrower road
that twisted downwards to a narrow plateau of
rock, perched above the booming surf of the
ocean.

The hideaway was a house, built on several
levels, tucked into the sheer rock face at the back
of the plateau. The arches and the roof of terra-
cotta tiles showed the usual Spanish influence, but
the furnishings inside were ultra-modern in
design, made from light-coloured wood and fine
printed cottons. Original paintings, mostly ab-
stracts by famous American painters, hung on the
walls. As in the ranch house of Myrna and Charles
Bixman there was everything that great wealth
could buy.

They sat on a low couch close to a wide patio
window from which they could look out at the
dark cavern of the sky arching over the glinting
ocean. Behind them in the dusky room, taped
music whispered softly—modern jazz played on
the piano by Dave Brubeck and on the saxophone
by Paul Desmond; followed by the guitar of
George Benson and then the trumpet of Chuck
Mangione; sophisticated modern music, yet no
less romantic in its way than the concerto and

serenade which Janos had played in the concert hall.

'Do you come here often?' Sara asked after sipping some of the fruit punch which had been brought to her by a dark-eyed, dark-haired Mexican-looking houseboy.

'Whenever the pressure of business lets up, which isn't as often as I would like,' said Glenn. 'Maybe I would come more often if I had someone to share it with.' He paused, then added pointedly, 'Someone like you.'

'It's in a lovely setting,' Sara remarked, with a touch of nervousness. Strange that she should feel nervous with Glenn. Until tonight she had felt at ease in his company. Since there was a considerable difference in their ages—she guessed he was about forty—she had more or less regarded him as an older brother figure or even as an uncle type.

'Do you have to go back to England so soon?' he asked.

'Yes. I've loved every minute of being here, but my holiday ends this coming weekend and I must return to work.'

'Is there someone over there, someone you love and are going to marry?' he asked.

'No.' She laughed a little as she looked at him in surprise. 'What's given you that idea?'

'A certain remoteness in you, a cool hands-off way you have of treating members of my sex,' he replied. 'So if you're not in love and are not going to be married the next question is—have you ever been married?'

'Yes.' Her voice was low and she kept her eyes down and her glance on the glass in her hand.

'And now you're divorced,' Glenn suggested.

'No, not yet.'

'Are you going to be?'

Again a vision of Magda Scott drifted before her inner eyes and she heard Janos asking herself if he could meet her somewhere to talk privately. To discuss a divorce? Probably.

'Perhaps,' she whispered. 'Why do you want to know?'

'I'd like to marry you.'

Sara lifted her head sharply and stared at him incredulously. In the soft indirect lighting his face was like a bronze cast under the waving silvery fair hair and his grey eyes were watching her closely.

'You're surprised?' he asked.

'Of course I am. We've only known each other a little over two weeks.'

'How long did you know the man you're married to before you agreed to marry him?' he challenged. 'Weeks, months, years before? Or was it only days?'

Disconcerted by the challenge, Sara avoided it by not answering and finishing the drink she held, remembering how quickly and easily Janos had wooed her and how she had been unable to withstand the fire of his passion. The drink finished, she set the empty glass down on the nearby occasional table and turning to Glenn said coolly,

'How long I knew him before I married him is

no concern of yours.'

'I like it,' he said, leaning towards her and smiling. 'I like the way you push me away. And of course you're right—it isn't any concern of mine. No more than my first marriage is any concern of yours. You do know I've been married, I guess?'

'Yes. Cecilia told me.'

'It's almost ten years since Tracy and I divorced, and Una, our daughter, is almost thirteen,' he told her.

'Does she live with her mother?' Sara asked politely.

'Most of the time, when she isn't away at private school. Sometimes she comes here to have a short holiday with me, but we don't get on too well. I'm afraid I haven't much patience with the behaviour of the adolescent. Would it bother you to have a teenage stepdaughter coming to stay for a few days every year?'

'I haven't said I'd marry you yet,' she retorted calmly.

'That's true. But I'm hoping you'll consider my proposal before you leave for England.'

'But I couldn't decide before Saturday,' she said quickly. 'I'll ... I'll have to get the divorce first and then see how I feel. I might not want to marry again.'

'You might not,' Glenn conceded. 'And I can understand that. After one disaster you're going to be wary of stepping into another. I felt the same way after my experience with Tracy. But now I know what I want from a wife and I believe you and I would make a good partnership. We have a lot in common.'

'Such as?' Sara challenged in her turn, looking round the luxurious room, thinking how different their backgrounds were. A member of a wealthy family, he had never known what it was to do without comfort and material possessions. He had never known what it was to suffer like Janos had suffered. Everything had come easily to him.

'We're both practical and cool-headed,' he said. 'For example, unlike my ex-wife you wouldn't get into a panic if I asked you to organise a dinner party for twenty guests at which the Governor of the State would be the guest of honour, would you?'

'No, I don't suppose I would,' she agreed.

'Now I'm not going to make any pretence of having fallen in love with you, Sara, or any of that nonsense,' he continued smoothly. 'Nor am I assuming you're in love with me. But I think we're both well-balanced adults who could live amicably together. I need hardly to tell you that if you married me you would live very comfortably. I would make you a generous allowance and I'm sure I could depend on you to run my homes properly, entertain my friends and business acquaintances and organise our leisure time together.'

'You wouldn't want me to continue with my own career, then?' she queried.

'Would you want to?'

'I enjoy designing very much and I don't think I could give it up just to stay at home and keep house.'

There was an awkward little silence, then Glenn spoke abruptly.

'Is it necessary for you to work for a textile company all the time? Could you freelance, create designs when you want to and then submit them to companies?'

It was something Sara had always hoped one day she would be able to do, but in Britain she had not had sufficient capital behind her to branch out on her own.

'Yes, I could ... if I had the right financial backing,' she replied.

'Marry me and you'll have it,' said Glenn, briskly businesslike. 'I'll place all my considerable expertise as the sales director of one of the biggest canning companies in the world at your disposal, and I'll promote your designs anywhere you want them promoted and in no time at all decor designers in this country will be insisting on furnishing fabrics designed by Sara Cranston. How about that as a basis for marriage? You continue with your career as a designer and I'll support you, provided that you do for me what I expect a wife to do.'

Practical, cool-headed, in control of himself and regarding falling in love as nonsense—and he saw her as being like that too. Sara shifted uneasily on the couch, remembering again with a sudden ache of regret Janos's swift passionate wooing of her.

Looking at Glenn, seeing the hardness of his face, it was difficult to imagine him in love or even making love. He would never even try to melt the ice in her veins or to rouse in her a passionate loving response as Janos had done so many times.

'So what do you think now?' he asked, leaning towards her. 'How do you like my offer?'

'I . . . I'll have to think about it,' she said evasively.

'Of course you will,' he agreed. 'And I wouldn't expect you to do anything else. How soon can you be divorced?'

'I'm not sure. I . . . I. . . .' She glanced at him and decided to be straight with him. 'I'll have to talk to Janos first.'

'Janos?' Glenn was quick to pounce on the name, his grey eyes glinting with surprise. 'You mean Vaszary?'

'Yes.'

'So that's how you knew he was married. Well, well, you certainly kept that a secret tonight, both of you! I was watching when Cecilia brought him to you and I would never have guessed you and he had once been intimate. How long since you separated?'

'Two years.'

'Did he leave you or did you leave him?'

'I . . . well, I suppose it was mutual.'

'Then you won't have too much trouble in getting a divorce since you haven't been living together.'

'No, I suppose we won't,' Sara replied. She

didn't care for all this cold-blooded discussion about a subject which she knew to be fraught with emotion, she decided, and rose to her feet. 'I must go back to Cecilia's house. She'll be wondering where I am.'

'It would also be a good idea if you could catch Vaszary before he returns to L.A.' Glenn said matter-of-factly, also rising to his feet. 'If you like I'll give Myrna a call on the phone and find out if he's still at her party. If he is you could speak to him and make some arrangement to meet him.'

'I . . . I . . . no, I'd rather write to him. There's no need for us to meet again. A divorce could be arranged without us meeting again.'

He turned to look at her, frowning slightly. Slowly he stepped towards her his grey eyes narrow as he studied her face.

'I think I'm beginning to understand why you wanted to get away from the concert hall and why you didn't want to go to the party,' he drawled. 'You're afraid of him?'

'No, I'm not,' Sara said quickly. 'I . . . I . . . just don't want to see him again, our marriage was only one of convenience, so he could stay in Britain after he'd escaped from Hungary. We mean nothing to each other and I expect he'll be as glad as I will to put an end to our legal association.'

Glenn gave her another shrewd assessing stare, then nodded, as if in understanding.

'Okay,' he drawled, 'then I won't call Myrna. Let me show you the rest of this place, just to whet your appetite for marriage to me,' he added lightly. 'Then when you're back in England you can think about it. Knowing what it's like might help you to make up your mind.'

It was almost one o'clock in the morning when Glenn's big car whispered its way along the grey driveway between the oleander shrubs to the Mertons' ranch-style bungalow which sprawled beside a sandy beach edging the ocean not far from Morro Bay. Although the outside lights were on no light shafted through the windows of the main living rooms or from any of the front bedrooms. Both Cecilia and her husband Philip were obviously back home, because their two cars were parked casually side by side in the driveway in front of the doors of the double garage.

'It looks as if they've gone to bed,' Sara whispered to Glenn.

'Can you get into the house easily, without disturbing them?' he asked.

'Yes. That's what's so convenient about this bungalow. All the rooms have patio windows opening on to the sun-deck. My room is at the back, facing the ocean.'

'I'll walk round there with you, just to make sure you get in safely,' he told her.

They walked up the steps to the wooden sun-deck as quietly as they could and along the side of the house to the corner were a light shone downwards, illuminating the soft sand of the beach. Beyond, the light surf twinkled as it hit the shore with a booming sound, then slithered back in long ripples of water. The patio window of Sara's room was dark, but light spilled out from the window of the room next to it. But even as she wondered who was sleeping in that room, the light went out.

'Thank you for coming with me,' Sara said to Glenn as she slid open the window. 'And thank you also for taking me to see your hideaway.'

'It was a pleasure,' he assured her, standing close to her. 'I hope you're going to consider my suggestion we marry seriously.'

'I will,' she replied coolly. 'Goodnight,' she added, lifting her face to him in unwitting invitation. Glen hesitated only a second or two, then bent his head and kissed her on the mouth.

'That also might help you to make up your mind,' he whispered. 'Goodnight, Sara. I'll see you again tomorrow.'

He waited until she had stepped into the room and had closed the sliding door, then he padded away along the deck. Letting out a sigh of relief, glad to be on her own again, Sara found her way across the room to the bedside lamp and flicked it on. Although it was late she didn't feel tired and she wished Cecilia had not gone to bed. She would have liked to have talked to her cousin, found out more about Myrna's party, whether Janos had gone to it with Magda Scott.

Oh, what did it matter to her if he had? What did it matter if he was having an affair with the beautiful film actress? Nothing at all. A noise behind her at the window made her turn round, thinking that Glenn had come back. Staring incredulously, she watched the window slide back and Janos step into the room. He slid the window closed behind him and turned to face her. He was wearing the dark evening trousers and the ruffled white shirt, but was without the tie, tail coat and cummerbund. The shirt was undone to the waist and its whiteness contrasted starkly with the golden brown hue of his skin and the gypsy blackness of his hair. He stood quite still with his back to the window, staring at her from under slanting eyebrows and she sensed a threat in his attitude. But then he had always spelt danger to her.

'What are you doing here?' she managed to exclaim.

'I have been waiting for you to return. Where have you been?' he replied softly, and began to walk across the room towards her.

'To the house of a friend.'

He stopped a few feet away from her, still watching her, his eyes glinting with yellow light.

'The friend who was kissing you just now, out there?' He jerked his head towards the window.

'Oh, I suppose you were in the next room, playing at peeping Tom,' she taunted.

'I was in the next room, yes,' he replied equably. 'I do not know what you mean when you talk about peeping Tom. I saw your friend kissing you when I stepped out on to the deck to come and talk to you. When I saw how friendly he was I waited, politely, until he had finished what he was doing and had left.' He paused, his glance drifting over her. 'I am glad you have come back tonight, Sara, and did not stay with your friend at his house. I hoped to see you at the party, but when you did not come to it I asked Cecilia if I could come back here with her. She invited me to stay the night. Why didn't you go to the party? Was it because you didn't want to see me?'

'I ... yes, it was,' Sara replied, turning away from him and going over to the dressing table, not wanting to look at him because to look at him was disturbing. She opened a drawer pretending she was looking for something and asked as casually as she could,

'Why did you want to see me?'

'I wanted to find out what you look like now, whether you are the same as I remember you,' Janos said softly, coming up behind her. 'You are the same and yet not the same,' he added. 'Your hair is in a different style and you use more make-up. You always were very poised and cool in company, but that poise used to be a cover for your shyness. Now it seems to be permanent,'

'Well, you couldn't really expect me to stay the same after ... after the way you tricked me into marrying you, could you?' she retorted, shutting the door with a bang and looking up at his reflection in the dressing table mirror, forcing herself to stare at him to look for changes in him and finding only that now he was carrying a little more weight and his cheeks were not quite so gaunt he was better-looking. His lips thinned and anger flared in his eyes as he stared back at her.

'I did not trick you into marrying me,' he retorted. 'You married me of your own free will.'

'But I wouldn't have done if ... if ... I'd known you'd come to England to marry Cecilia,' she argued.

'Wouldn't you?' he jeered. 'Oh, I think you would have done. You were longing to be loved, aching to be married,' he taunted cruelly.

'I suppose you want a divorce now, so you can marry someone else,' she said coldly, swinging round to face him and leaning her hips against the dressing table.

'I want whatever you want,' he replied. 'By now you should know what that is. I've given you long enough to make up your mind.'

'I made it up two years ago,' she flared. 'And I haven't changed it. But I'm tired now and I'd like to go to bed.'

'Don't let me stop you.' Janos's smile mocked her. 'I'll sit here.' He sat down in an armchair and draped a long leg over one of the arms. 'And you can lie in bed and we'll talk.'

'I'm not going to get undressed and into bed while you're in this room,' she hissed at him. 'Get out!'

'You always were a prude,' he taunted.

'Janos, please, go to your own room. I promise to see you in the morning. We can talk then.'

'No, we'll talk now. It is morning already,' he retorted serenely, and his eyes laughed at her between their thick lashes. 'Don't be shy, darling, get undressed and into bed.'

'But won't your pillow-friend be wondering where you are?' she countered sweetly.

'Pillow-friend?' His dark eyebrows slanted into a bar across the bridge of his nose. 'What is a pillow-friend?'

'Oh, don't pretend you don't know,' she replied scathingly. 'Your latest affair, then—Magda Scott. I'm sure Cecilia couldn't avoid having to invite her to stay the night here too.'

All mockery had faded from Janos's face. He looked suddenly very bitter, his mouth drawn down at the corners his eyes without light.

'I wonder why it is you are always ready to believe what other people say about me,' he said wearily. 'Magda is not here. She has gone back to Beverly Hills. If you do not believe me then go into the next room and look. Or wake your cousin and ask her if Magda is here.' He paused, then added in the same flat tones, 'She is not what someone told you she is. I do not have an affair with her.'

'But she wants to marry you,' Sara accused.

'Does she? Who told you that? Your friend? The one who kissed you a few minutes ago outside the window? Perhaps he is *your* latest affair, a successor to Tom Caldwell?'

'I didn't have an affair with Tom Caldwell,' she flared. 'And I'm not having an affair with Glenn Bixman.'

'Why should I believe you when I see with my

own eyes that he kisses you like a lover?' he jeered. 'And you do not resist. You do not slap his face for taking advantage.'

'He didn't kiss me like a lover,' she retorted, and seeing his mouth curl with scepticism turned away from him muttering, 'Oh, you wouldn't understand. I wish you'd go away, back to your own room, and let me go to bed. We're neither of us making any sense. We'll be able to discuss a divorce much more rationally when we've both had some sleep.'

'I do not wish to discuss divorce,' said Janos tonelessly.

Sara swung round to face him again and found he had stood up. Tall and graceful in black and white, looking at her in that way she had seen him look at her so many times, as if she were the only woman in the world for him, he was a threat to her hard-won peace of mind.

'But you said you wanted to talk,' she whispered.

'About us, yes,' he agreed, coming towards her. 'Silly talk, pillow talk with a pillow-friend if you like, before we go to sleep together.'

'No—no!' Turning away, Sara clapped her hands over her ears. 'I don't want to hear you. I don't want to see you. Go away, go away. Janos, please go away!' Her hands left her ears when she felt his knuckles brush against the skin at her nape as he lifted the tab of the zip which fastened the back of her dress. Too late she tried to turn to face him so that he couldn't undo the zip. It opened with a hiss.

'Oh, why did you do that?' she cried, her hands at the back of the dress trying to find the tab of the zip so she could do it up again, turning her back to him again.

'So I could do this,' he said softly, and his hands slid inside the dress to cup her breasts. 'Your skin is still as white as milk,' he murmured, 'and you still have a scattering of tiny golden freckles across the top of your shoulders. I have missed those freckles. I have missed every part of you.' His lips burned against the side of her throat.

Sara swayed where she stood, weakened suddenly by the familiar sensations that tingled along her nerves. Fighting the surge of passionate desire flooding through her, moaning half in distress and half in pleasure, she twisted from side to side in an effort to free herself.

'Please let me go,' she muttered. 'Please let me go. I want my freedom.'

For a moment Janos released her, but only so he could spin her round to face him and before she could back away from him his hands were curving about her waist. His face loomed over her, the tawny eyes sultry beneath heavy lids, the well-shaped lips sensually parted.

'Freedom from what?' he asked.

'From . . . from you,' she whispered. Her hands were behaving strangely. They seemed to have a will of their own and she was having to clench them to prevent them from reaching out to slide within the opening of his shirt and caress his hair-roughened chest. Her body, too, was softening to the thrust of his hips against it.

'Why?' he murmured, lifting a hand from her waist to the right shoulder of her dress which, because the dress was unzipped, was already beginning to slip down her arm. Slowly he began to slide it even further, right off her arm and over her clenched hand.

'To ... to marry someone else,' she replied, lifting her other arm obligingly so that he could slide the dress off that too.

'The man who was here with you just now?' he asked softly, busy with the belt at her waist, unbuckling it and then sliding the dress slowly and suggestively over her hips until it fell with a whisper of sound to the floor.

'Yes,' Sara replied. Now that he had taken her dress and she was wearing only a wisp of a bra and brief panties, it seemed the last of her restraints were slipping away, overborne by another onrush of sensuousness. 'What are you going to do now?' she whispered, giving in to desire and lifting her arms about his neck, delighted by the silkiness of the hair that grew thickly at the nape of his neck as her fingers tangled in it, while her body pressed against his invitingly.

'I'm going to put you to bed,' he replied, laughter shaking in his voice. 'And then I'm going to do what I wanted to do that morning I returned to London, what I should have done then.'

For a few seconds sanity returned to her and she tried to pull away, but Janos's arms tightened around her and he lifted her easily to carry her to the bed.

'No, no!' she cried, struggling to get free, kicking with her legs. 'You don't understand. Glenn has asked me to marry him, so . . . so . . . I'd like a divorce. I don't want you. I don't want to go to bed with you!'

'You want it, so stop pretending you don't,' he growled savagely. 'And scratching my face won't stop me from taking what I want. Nothing is going to stop me tonight. You may talk as much as you like about wanting your freedom, but you're still mine . . .'

'I'm not. I'm not! I don't belong to any man,' Sara spluttered as Janos laid her on the bed. Vainly she rolled over and clawed her way to the other side in an attempt to escape. Immediately he was after her, long arms reaching round her to haul her back to the middle of the bed. Kneeling with one leg on either side of her, he loomed over her like a dark avenging angel.

'You're still mine.' His voice was thick with passion and his eyes glittered dangerously. 'And tonight I'm going to have you.'

'But not against my will,' she retorted, but there was no defiance in her voice, in fact it slurred sensuously.

'It won't be against your will, my sweet, shy Sara,' he whispered, and the laughter was back in his voice, warming it. He framed her face with gentle long-fingered hands, turning her towards him as he lay down beside her. For a moment his eyes, heavy and opaque with sadness, gazed into hers and his mouth twisted as if with sudden pain. 'God, if you knew how much I have longed to see you, be with you, talk with you these past two years—if you knew you wouldn't . . .' His voice cracked, his breath came out on a long hissing sigh and his parted lips covered hers.

At first there was no tenderness in his kiss, nothing to soften its raw violence. It punished and insulted her. Yet Sara didn't resist. Instead a similar violence surged up in her as every hidden potent nerve in her body demanded to be titillated into throbbing agony which could be released in only one way, in complete explosive union with him. Her fingers tore at his shirt, found their way to the fastening of his trousers, and at last they were close, legs entwining, hands stroking, skin rubbing skin, mouths feeding hungrily until the tenderness which had always been a part of their lovemaking broke through the violence, like a sweet high melody played on a violin breaks through the noisy discordant blare of brass and the throbbing passionate chords of cellos.

Afterwards they slept, lying close on the tangled bed. Sara wakened first to filtered daylight vying with the rosy glow which still shafted down from the bedside lamp. Lifting an arm, she switched off the lamp, noted that the time was a quarter to eight and lay for a moment in drowsy contentment listening to the sound of Janos's regular breathing, the distant singing of Aurora, Cecilia's Mexican cook, and the high-pitched chatter of Paul, Cecilia's and Philip's little boy.

A baby. The thought flashed through Sara's mind, jolting her. Her hand went to her flat stomach. After what had happened last night there was a strong possibility that she could have conceived. She turned her head and looked at Janos. He was very close to her and his eyes were open, watching her. Was it her imagination or was there calculation in their expression? Clear they were, like an eagle's. Predatory. A shiver of revulsion shook her and she groaned, remembering how easily she had responded to his lovemaking, how happily and with what abandonment she had made love to him during the night. If she did conceive she would have no one to blame but herself.

'Remember the Pheasant Inn?' he murmured, shifting closer to her, lifting a bare leg across both of hers and sliding a hand up over her breast to her throat to stroke the curve of her cheek with one finger.

'Do you?' she asked, her breath catching in her throat.

'Many times I have remembered it when I have lain awake at night in some hotel room in a strange noisy city where I have performed at a concert. I remember there was a house beside a lake. It was for sale and we looked in at the windows to see what it was like inside and we talked of how we would renovate it one day when we could afford to buy it. Remember, Sara?'

Oh, God, what was he doing to her? Not only did he want her body, but he wanted to tear her heart out too, with his reference to those happy hours they had spent together in the Lake District and the implication that he had been lonely and unhappy when he had lain awake in hotel rooms. He was doing what he had always done, playing on her sympathy, seducing her into believing that he loved her as he had seduced her three years ago, pretending. Oh, she couldn't bear it any longer.

'No, I don't remember, and I don't want to remember,' she said coldly, shifting to the edge of the bed and swinging off it. Going to the closet, she took out her dressing gown and wrapped it round herself, tying the belt tightly, keeping her back to him.

'I'd like to go back there, to the Lake District in the summer,' he said quietly.

'It rains a lot,' she said shortly, and went over to the patio window to look out. It was another golden Californian morning. The Pacific Ocean looked smooth and milky blue, edged with lacy surf that tumbled on to soft pale sand.

'I'd like to buy a house there, beside a lake, a house I could go back to live in when I'm not playing in concerts or making records or giving master classes at schools of music.' Janos's voice was still quietly determined.

'I'm sure Magda Scott wouldn't like it,' said Sara, still looking out of the window.

He made no comments and she heard the bed creak as he left it. Half turning, she watched him pull on his trousers and fasten them. Picking up his ruffled shirt, he slung it over one shoulder and came towards the patio window to stand beside her. Immediately aware of his warmth, of the sheen on his skin, the healthy male smell of him, Sara stepped sideways away from danger.

'I have to leave in half an hour to go back to L.A. From there I'll be flying to Mexico City to play in a concert. How much longer are you going to be here?' he asked.

'I'm leaving the day after tomorrow. I have to be back at work on Monday next.' Sara kept her gaze steadily averted from him and watched the perpetual advance and retreat of the sparkling surf.

'After Mexico I go back to New York to give master classes at a school of music there. I won't be through until the end of June,' he told her. 'But I could be in Manchester in July. We could go to the Lake District then and look for that house.'

'We? What makes you think I'll want to have anything to do with helping you to find a house?'

'We are married. You are my wife.' There was an edge of irritation in his voice.

'Don't you think you're assuming too much. Just because we've met again, accidentally, and you've been able to force me to submit to your physical demands, you're assuming that I'm ready to live with you again whenever you happen to be in the same country as me. Well, last night changed nothing.'

'I didn't force you to do anything,' said Janos between his teeth. 'You wanted to make love as much as I did. We couldn't help it after being apart for so long.'

'Speak for yourself!' she snapped.

'*I* couldn't help it, then,' he said exasperatedly.' But I'm not apologising for what happened. I hadn't seen you for two years . . .'

'Something you could have remedied any time you wanted to,' she flung at him, turning to face him, her voice shaking a little as she remembered how often she had longed for him to turn up at the flat in Manchester. 'I know you've been in England, recording in London. And last August you were at the Edinburgh Festival.'

'You seem to be very knowledgeable about my engagements,' he jeered, his mouth curling sardonically. 'But haven't you forgotten something? Two years ago you told me you didn't want to see me again—ever, so I stayed away from you. I have a certain amount of pride, too, you know. Not until you invited me was I going to come and see you again. And we wouldn't have met last night if I had not been invited by the local symphony orchestra to play.'

'Oh, yes, of course. Music always comes first with you, doesn't it? It always has and always will, people don't really matter . . . except when they can be used . . . like . . . like you used me.' Sara's voice shook again and she turned away. 'And if I asked you not to go to Los Angeles and Mexico City now you'd refuse, wouldn't you? You wouldn't stay with me.'

'And you wouldn't come with me, if I asked you, would you?' he retorted. 'You would rather go back to Manchester and work in a mill.'

She turned again to face him.

'I like designing,' she whispered. 'I have to do it.'

'And I am compelled to play music for the public. It is what I do best. There is no other life for me,' he replied.

'You don't love me,' she accused.

'And I am beginning to realise, at last, that you don't and never have loved me,' he said bitterly, and turning away he slid open the patio window. 'Goodbye, Sara,' he said, and stepping through the opening walked away along the sun-deck to the next room.

For a while Sara stayed where she was looking out at the beach, watching the play of sunlight and shadow on the sand and the sea, hearing only vaguely the noises of the house, the murmur of voices, the throb of a car's engine and then a silence as if everyone had gone away. Unaware of the passage of time, she struggled to suppress a strong instinctive urge to throw all her clothes into her suitcase and go with Janos to Los Angeles and then to Mexico City, warning herself that to do so would be to lower herself in her own esteem. She would be giving in not only to his physical demands but also to her own, and that wasn't the path of true love. It was too easy.

But when someone knocked on the bedroom door she turned hopefully towards it. Had Janos come back to insist that she go with him, to overwhelm her again with seduction? She hurried across to the door and opened it. Disappointment when she saw Cecilia standing there stabbed through her, creating a raw ache somewhere inside.

'Hi,' said Cecilia, stepping into the room. She was carrying a breakfast tray. 'I thought you might like to have breakfast in here. Aurora is spring-cleaning the kitchen today and everything is in a mess.' She set the tray down on the bedside table and began to pour coffee into two mugs. Taking her own mug, she sank down in the armchair. 'What happened to you after the interval last night? Why didn't you come to Myrna's party?'

'Surely you can guess,' said Sara dryly, picking up the other mug of coffee and sitting on the side of the bed.

'You didn't want to see Janos,' said Cecilia.

'Right first time.'

'Why?'

'Because . . . oh, why didn't you tell me he'd be a soloist at the concert?' Sara demanded. 'How could you be so cruel not to warn me?' She was having difficulty in keeping her voice calm and low. One night with Janos and her emotions were bursting out in all directions, completely out of her control.

'I had this feeling that if you knew he'd be performing you wouldn't go to the concert. And I don't think I was being cruel. I thought I was being kind, bringing you two together again, even if it was only for a short time. You know you've been pining for him for the past two years.'

'I haven't been pining,' Sara protested.

'Oh, yes, you have. You've been all frozen up inside and you've had that raw look about you that a woman gets when she's missing something she once possessed, the satisfaction she once had from being made love to by the man she loves. And I thought Janos looked pretty grim too, when I met him in L.A. He wasn't at all like he was in Salzburg, full of mischief and jokes. And I could see he was heartily sick of that Magda woman hanging on to his coat-tails last night. That's why I invited him to come back here and stay the night with us. I gave him the bedroom next to this one.'

'I wonder you didn't put him in this room straight away,' said Sara tartly. 'He slept here.'

'Mmm, it looks like it.' A mischievous grin curved Cecilia's full lips as her bright eyes roved over the tumbled bed. 'Then everything is all right?' She tipped her head to one side. 'Yes, you do look better, in spite of the lines under your eyes. You're not quite so raw-looking.'

'Oh, stop it! You talk as if . . . as if sexual satisfaction was all that mattered in life!' Close to tears for the first time in her life, Sara hurled a pillow in protest at her cousin. 'And everything isn't all right. Nothing has changed—nothing. I'm still second fiddle, the woman he . . . he sleeps with only when I happen to be in the right place at the right time and whom he married because marriage was the only way he could stay in Britain. He doesn't love me and I don't love him.' Sara paused while she struggled to control her voice. 'He's gone, hasn't he?' she added tonelessly.

'Yes, he left about fifteen minutes ago. I thought you might have gone with him.'

'I . . . I . . . wasn't invited to go,' Sara sniffed, then wiped her eyes with the back of her hand and drank more coffee.

'Oh, Sara, you are a fool, a silly stubborn fool,' sighed Cecilia.

'I was a fool to marry him and now I'm a fool because I don't follow him about, hanging on to his coat-tails like Magda Scott,' said Sara, her voice rasping with bitterness. 'So I'm a fool.' She shrugged.

'Anyway, where did you go last night with Glenn?' asked Cecilia.

'To his house at Big Sur. He . . . he asked me to marry him.'

'My God!' exclaimed Cecilia. 'But you can't marry him. You're married to Janos. What are you going to do?'

'I'm going to get a divorce,' said Sara, her voice flat and cold.

CHAPTER SIX

'It's lovely to see you again. I'm so glad you were able to come to lunch.'

Ida Williams's voice was warm with affection as she greeted Sara in the foyer of one of Manchester's best known hotels.

'And I'm glad you thought of phoning me and inviting me to come. It's ages since we last met. What are you doing here. Is Gareth with you?' asked Sara.

'No. He flew back to London this morning. We've been touring Scotland by car and we came back by way of the Lake District, arriving here last night. There was a message waiting for him when we got here to say that his father had been taken ill, so he's gone ahead without me and I'll take my time driving back. I did want to see you. How are you?'

'Very well, thank you,' Sara lied as she sat down at the round table to which they had been shown. 'You haven't chosen a very good day for your visit.'

'Yes, it is wet, isn't it? It rained all the time we were in the Lakes too.'

They both studied the menus which had been brought and gave their order to the waiter. For a few moments they chatted, exchanging information about what they had both been doing.

'And so that's the end of our holiday for this year,' sighed Ida as she finished telling Sara about the route she and Gareth had taken through Scotland. 'It was heaven to have Gareth to myself for a while, just the two of us visiting the places we've always wanted to visit, poking about old brochs and other historical ruins.'

'Davina wasn't with you, then?'

'No. Davina has been in New York, at the Juillard, taking violin classes. She's returning on Friday next.'

'She has been studying with Janos, I suppose.'

'No.' Ida looked up and studied Sara's face. 'You didn't hear about the accident?' she queried, a frown of puzzlement creasing her forehead.

'What accident?' Sara's knees went weak suddenly. 'Janos had an accident?' she muttered. Her mouth felt dry. 'I ... I ... haven't heard anything about him since I was in California. That was when he told me he would be giving the classes in New York.'

'You saw him?' Ida seemed more puzzled than ever.

'We met, not for very long. What was the accident, Ida? Please tell me!'

'There was a fire, a very serious fire, in the building in New York where he was living and he suffered some burns,' Ida told her. It was so typical of him. He could have escaped from the building without injury, but he had to go and help someone else, an old lady who was trapped in her apartment by the smoke. His hands were badly burned.'

'Oh, no!' Sara felt her face go white and she had to swallow the sickness that rose in her throat. His hands—his beautiful hands, with their magical flexible fingers which could produce such perfect notes on the violin. Vaguely she heard Ida exclaiming, calling to a waiter. A glass containing golden liquor appeared before her. She grabbed it and sipped. The brandy coursed down her throat, searing it.

'Sara, are you all right?'

Ida's face swam into focus. Her dark blue eyes searched Sara's face anxiously.

'I'm sorry,' said Ida. 'It was my fault. I thought you would know. I thought he would have contacted you and told you or asked someone else to tell you. After all, you are his wife and you have a right to know.'

'Not any more,' Sara muttered, staring down at the brandy. 'I mean I'm still married to him in the legal sense, but I don't have the right to know when he's been hurt or anything like that. You see, I filed for a divorce as soon as I returned from California.'

'Does he know you have?'

'He must know. My lawyer wrote to him to inform him. We haven't heard from him yet or from his lawyer, but I suppose if he's been hurt he hasn't been able to write or . . . where is he? Still in hospital? Do you know?'

'Yes, I know,' said Ida slowly. 'In fact Gareth and I visited him two days ago. He's living in the Lake District. He's bought a house there.'

'Where? Near a place called Millwater?'

'That's right. It's quite an old house, needs a

lot of renovation. When he came to England at
the beginning of July he told us he was coming
north to look for a house while his hands were
still recuperating. Naturally I assumed he'd be
coming to you first and you'd be house-hunting
together and I was very surprised to find him
living there alone.'

Ida paused because the waiter had appeared
with their lunch. She waited until everything was
set before them and he had gone before she leaned
across the table and said in a low voice, 'Gareth
and I are extremely concerned about him. He
doesn't seem to be making any effort to exercise
his fingers to make them better so he can play
again. I don't think he's touched the violin since
the accident. It's as if the shock of being burned
has numbed part of him, the sensitive, creative
part, the musician in him. He says he doesn't care
if he never plays on the concert platform again.'
Ida paused again, looked down at the plate of meat
and vegetables which was on the table in front of
her. 'I'm not the sort of person who likes to interfere in anyone else's life,' she said, 'because I
don't like anyone to interfere in mine. But this is
one time when I feel I have to do something.
Otherwise the world is going to lose a very gifted
musician. Sara, please will you go and see Janos?'

Sara picked up her knife and fork, pretending
to be interested in the food.

'I can't,' she said abruptly.

'Why not? You're not divorced from him yet,'
said Ida sharply.

'I know. But if I go and see him he'll ...' Sara broke off, shaking her head. 'He'll take advantage of the situation,' she muttered.

'I know you and he have had your problems,' Ida continued. 'But then no marriage is perfect and most of us manage to resolve our differences over the years. I've always hoped that you and Janos would, you're so suited to each other.'

'You think so? In what ways?'

'Well, you're calm and collected, sensible with a lot of strong inner resources, the perfect wife and companion, I would say, for a lively, passionate, talented person like Janos. You're an anchor, so to speak, in the wild tempestuous storm of his life.'

'But anchors don't have feelings and I do,' whispered Sara. 'And Janos hurt them by pretending to marry me for love when all the time he was marrying me because he had to get married to someone ... anyone ... as long as she was a citizen of this country.'

Ida laid down her knife and fork, leaned her elbows on the table and rested her chin on her hands. The expression in her eyes was one of exasperated pity.

'Do you know what you're talking about?' she asked, 'because I'm sure I don't. Why did Janos have to marry ... anyone ... as long as she was a citizen of this country?'

'So he could stay here. He had it all planned before he came here. He'd arranged with my cousin Cecilia when he met her in Salzburg that if he could ever get away from Hungary and come to this country she would marry him so he could claim immigrant status as her husband. When he arrived he found out from me that she was married already. But he didn't tell me he'd made that arrangement with her. He just went ahead and ... and persuaded me to marry him.' Sara's voice quavered and faded.

'Who told you he had an arrangement with Cecilia?' asked Ida. 'Did she?'

'No. Do you remember the day before the New Century Orchestra returned from that tour of the States and you invited me to meet Elisabeth Herrenhoff?'

'I remember.' Ida's eyes glinted with comprehension. 'She believed you were your cousin, the little English girl Janos had met in Salzburg who'd promised to marry him.'

'That's right. And then Davina told me later she'd overheard Gareth telling Janos when he first visited your house to go and get married and then he'd be able to offer him a position in the orchestra.'

'And you believed Davina?' Ida looked astounded. 'Knowing how infatuated she was with him at the time and how jealous she was of you, you believed her? Sara, how could you be so foolish!'

'I didn't want to believe her, but what she said fitted in with everything else I knew about Janos. Tom Caldwell, for whom I used to work, was always suspicious of him.' Sara hesitated for a moment, fiddling with her fork. 'I suppose the truth of it is I was always unsure of Janos because I couldn't believe that someone like him, out of the ordinary, a brilliant musician with a great future, could possibly be in love with someone ordinary and dull like me,' she added. 'Even Davina guessed he didn't love me and would leave me, and she was right.'

'But didn't you ask Janos if there was any truth in what Elisabeth had said?' Ida queried.

'Yes, I did. I asked him if Cecilia and he had arranged to get married and he said he couldn't deny it. Then we quarrelled—and you know the rest. I came back here and he went to the States.'

'And you continued to believe he'd deceived you,' Ida sighed exasperatedly and leaned across the table again. 'Now listen to me,' she said authoritatively. 'Janos didn't have to marry you or anyone else to stay in this country. Oh, I know he made an arrangement with Cecilia, but that was done because he was afraid at that time he would be granted only a visitor's permit to come here. But in the end he came as an accepted immigrant because Gareth and several other eminent musicians in this country, who had met him, sponsored him.'

'Davina said she heard her father tell Janos to get married,' argued Sara stubbornly.

'Davina heard only half a story—or preferred to tell you only half a story in order to upset you. When Janos first came to Gareth in London he told us how he'd met you and wanted to marry

·you. He was excited and impatient, so Gareth told him to come back here and marry you before he joined the orchestra. Gareth guessed that Janos wouldn't settle down to regular rehearsals and performances until he was sure of you.' Ida sighed again. 'If only you'd told me about your doubts and suspicions I could have told you what I know. Why didn't you?'

'I . . . I . . . don't know. I suppose I thought you believed he'd married me for convenience and that you approved,' Sara muttered.

'I had no idea you felt so insecure in yourself,' Ida remarked. 'You give the impression of being sure of yourself, of knowing what you want and where you're going. But it's that inner insecurity which has made you doubt Janos. You can't believe he loves you, because you don't love yourself very much. And you don't love him because you don't know how to love. No one has ever shown you how.'

'That isn't true! I do love him . . . I mean, I did love him,' muttered Sara. 'I worshipped him,' she added in a whisper.

'And stopped worshipping him when you found out he was only human after all,' Ida derided.

'Ida, will you please tell me exactly where he's living?'

'All right. The house is in Milldale, close to Millwater. It's called, as you might expect, the Mill House. Now it's up to you. The next move is yours. If you want to talk to Janos you'll have to go and see him, because I can tell you now, he'll never come to see you. He's proud, much more proud than any of us are, and you've offended him greatly by rejecting him twice and there's a strong possibility he'll never forgive you. Now what would you like for dessert?'

For the next few days and nights Sara went over and over again everything Janos had said to her before they had married, during the quarrel in London before they had separated and when they had met in California, and eventually admitted to herself that she had made a mistake in jumping to the conclusion that he had married her in haste to gain immigrant status.

Having admitted that she had acted foolishly and out of jealousy when she had walked out on him in London, she felt more able to consider the pros and cons concerning the renewal of their marriage. Deep down she knew she wanted to rush off at once to Milldale and tell Janos she had been wrong and ask him if they could start all over again. But then she would begin to imagine his reaction to her arrival. Supposing he refused to listen to her apology? Supposing he rejected her as she had rejected him? She would be mortified, she knew she would. Wouldn't it be better then to pretend she didn't know where he was? To forget what Ida had told her and continue with the divorce proceedings?

Days and nights of torment made her tired and affected her work. She became short-tempered with the people she worked with, drank too much coffee and lost her appetite.

'What the hell is the matter with you?' Tom Caldwell demanded, striding into her office which had once been his office. 'I'm getting complaints about you from all sides. What's up, Sara? Still having marital problems?'

'What if I am?' she retorted. 'It's no business of yours.'

'It is if it affects your work and your treatment of the people who work with you. Evans in the printing department is complaining that you've changed your mind three times about the colour combinations for that new foxglove design. We can't have that, Sara. It's a waste of time and money we can't afford.'

'Then perhaps you can't afford me any more,' she flung at him.

'And what's that supposed to mean?'

'I'm leaving . . resigning.' Not at all surprised at her sudden decision, recognising that it had been forming in her mind ever since she had returned from California, Sara began to collect up sheets of paper on which she had been trying out designs and pushed them into her briefcase.

'Not now!' exclaimed Tom.

'Yes, now. Right this minute. I'll write a formal letter and post it to you tomorrow—that is if I have time.'

'Sara, wait—don't do anything hastily.' Tom came towards her. 'You know what happens when you act on impulse. You always make a mistake, like you did when you married Vaszary. And I've often blamed myself for that. If I could have stopped you from taking him to Stonethwaite with you that time he wouldn't have been able to persuade you to marry him and you wouldn't be in the mess you are now.'

'If you're to blame for anything, Tom, it's for being suspicious of him and making me suspicious,' she retorted. 'And the mistake I made was in listening to what you and other people said about him instead of listening to him and my own heart.'

'But you can't just walk out of Ferris's like this. You'll lose the rest of this month's salary if you do,' he protested, following her to the door.

'I don't care. I've been thinking of leaving for some time. I'm going to freelance, submit my designs wherever I feel like submitting them.'

'You'll starve,' he jeered. 'You're not well known enough to freelance yet.'

'Maybe I'll go somewhere where I know I can freelance without starving,' Sara retorted, going past him and out through the door.

'Where?' he rapped.

'California,' she replied lightly. 'Goodbye, Tom.'

She felt ridiculously lighthearted and lightheaded as she went out into the mill-yard where the cars were parked. As she started her car she glanced at her watch. It was only two-thirty on a mild sunny afternoon, and she experienced a sudden revulsion of feeling towards her flat. She wasn't going back there to be racked again by indecision and backward thinking, and it was a long time since she had driven north, to the countryside she loved. She would drive to Stonethwaite and perhaps lose herself somewhere among the green dales, timeless stone villages and shimmering lakes.

She took the old way through Preston and Lancaster to Kendal, and a light rain was falling when at last she found the fragile, narrow road to Millwater along which she and Janos had driven one snowy night over three years previously. It twisted through a desolate moonscape of brown moorland, big boulders and loose stone screes and Sara had to shift into the lowest gear for the long pull up the slope to the Pheasant Inn. The rain stopped just as she was passing the old building and the sun peeped out from behind the gauzy grey clouds which were lifting from the tops of the fells to shine on the white walls.

Over the crest of the hill the car swooped and down a glistening grey road into a vivid green valley hemmed in by high ridges of rock. Caught in the bottom of the valley a small lake twinkled with blue and silver light and beyond the valley, in the distance, the tawny shoulders of a familiar mountain dominated the western skyline.

Behind the old weathered house which was situated among clustering elm trees sunlight shifted across the undulating land, marking every fold with deep shadow. Tiny becks wound like silver threads across the flanks of upland sheep pastures criss-crossed by rough stone walls.

Sara parked the car in front of the house and

sat for a while staring at the rough moss-covered blocks of stone from which it was built. She was still surprised that Janos had been able to buy the house, not because she had thought he wouldn't have enough money—he must have earned several hundred thousands of pounds over the past three years—but because she had thought the house would have been sold long ago. But perhaps no one had fancied spending money on an old broken-down place tucked away in Milldale, one of the more remote dales of the Lake District.

From the outside it was difficult to tell if the place was inhabited, but there was a car parked in front of a barnlike building which must have once been a stable. Sara approached the front door and rang the bell. When no one came she banged on the knocker. Then when there was still no answer she walked round to the back of the house, found the back door, lifted up the latch, pulled it open and stepped inside.

The kitchen was in a chaotic condition and judging by the pile of dishes in the sink no one had washed up for a few days. Sara felt a prick of alarm. Supposing Janos was ill and was lying in bed, unable to fend for himself? Quickly she went through the kitchen into the empty, echoing hall-way. Light slanting in through the fanlight over the doorway showed up the dusty floor.

'Hello! Anyone at home?' she called, and looked into the first room on her left. To her surprise it was newly decorated and smelling still of paint. A new dining table was in the middle of the floor with six chairs set around it. A sideboard took up the whole of one wall. Dark blue velvet curtains draped the long french windows which looked out over the overgrown lawn.

Going out into the hall again, she moved into the room on the opposite side. Running the full depth of the house with windows at both ends, it was in the process of being renovated. Someone had been plastering the walls and the ceiling in readiness for decoration and there were rolls of wallpaper stacked in a corner.

Sara stepped out into the hall again and looked up the stair well. The stairs were uncarpeted and someone had carried a can of paint up them recently, which had been open, because there were blobs of wet paint all the way up. Slowly she began to go up the stairs.

When she reached the top landing she listened. From behind one of the closed doors came the swishing sound of someone using either a paint roller or a paintbrush.

'Janos!' she called. 'Where are you?'

The swishing sound stopped.

'Who is there?' It was definitely Janos who spoke.

'It . . . it's me. Sara.'

'Who?'

'Sara.' She walked towards the door of the room from which his voice came, turned the knob and pushed the door open. It collided with something behind it and she pushed harder.

'No, wait! Don't . . .' Janos began to swear in

Hungarian as whatever was behind the door gave way and crashed to the floor.

'Oh, what's happened?' Frantically Sara pushed against the door, forcing it open against the aluminium step-ladder which had fallen down. Looking round the edge of the door, she saw Janos sitting on the floor staring at a pool of white paint which had spilled. His dark hair was sprinkled with paint and he was wearing an old paint-spattered shirt and jeans. Rubber gloves covered his hands. 'What are you doing?' she gasped.

'I was painting the ceiling until you pushed open the door and knocked the ladder from beneath me,' he said dryly, getting to his feet. 'Couldn't you have waited until I had got down and moved the ladder away before trying to come in?'

'Well, how was I to know what you were doing? When I couldn't find you downstairs I thought you might be lying in bed ill. I didn't know you could paint.'

'I'm not very good at it, but I'm learning, by doing,' he replied.

'But surely you aren't going to redecorate the whole house yourself?' exclaimed Sara. Never in all the time she had lived with Janos had he shown any desire, let alone any ability, to do anything practical.

'Do I detect a note of sarcasm?' he retorted. 'Are you hinting that I'm not able to do it?'

'No . . . no,' she said hastily. 'I'm surprised, that's all. There seems to be such a lot to do for one person, I mean.'

'I have help. George Kent's brother is a house-builder and he and his son are doing most of the heavy work like re-plastering and insulating and putting in new plumbing and heating. Only this week they are away on holiday, so I thought I would try to paint this bedroom. It's a way of passing the time.' Janos shrugged and gave her an underbrowed glance. 'Who told you I was here?' he asked coolly.

'Ida Williams.'

'Damn her!' His eyes glinted angrily.

'That's not a very nice thing to say,' she rebuked him. 'I had lunch with her in Manchester and she said she and Gareth had been here to see you.'

'And I told them not to tell anyone of my whereabouts,' he retorted. 'Not even you.'

'Why not? Why didn't you want me to know you were here?' In the face of his cool, slightly mocking reception her pride was building up. Yet what had she hoped for? To be welcomed with open arms? To be told he needed her and couldn't manage without her? Contrary to the image she had built up of him from what Ida had told her, he seemed to be managing very well. There were no signs of neglect in his face and he seemed to have come to terms with the state of his hands.

'No, not yet,' he replied smoothly. 'I want to keep this place a secret until it is completely re-novated and fit to live in. Then I might issue invitations to a few select people, and you might be among them.'

'Oh, then I'm sorry I've intruded,' Sara retorted, pride and anger flaring up together, and turning on her heel she left the room and hurried along the landing to the stairs, berating herself because she had made a fool of herself after all. She had lowered her pride and had come, and Janos didn't want her.

As she went down the stairs as fast as she could she heard a lot of noise coming from the bedroom as he moved the ladder. She was in the hall and crossing it to the front door before he caught up with her.

'You can't get out of the house that way,' he said. 'The door is jammed and won't open.'

Blindly she turned to make her way to the kitchen and out of the back door, only to find he was blocking the way.

'Please let me pass,' she muttered, not looking at him.

'Not until you have told me why you have come here.'

'I'm on my way to Stonethwaite to visit my aunt and as it's such a lovely day I thought I'd drive round this way to see what it's like in the summer,' she replied stiffly, keeping her glance down and staring at his gloved hands. 'Ida told me that you'd hurt your hands in a fire,' she added, 'and I...'

'Came to see if it is true.' There was a note of bitter mockery in his voice as he raised his hands and began to pull the gloves off them. 'Well, it is. Have a good look,' he taunted.

They were badly blotched and there were ugly white seams where plastic surgery had been done. Sickness welled up in Sara and she swayed as faintness overcame her. She covered her face with her hands.

'Oh, how could you!' she muttered. 'How could you do that to yourself?'

'I could hardly leave an old lady to die of asphyxiation and burning when I was capable of getting into her room and dragging her out of it, could I?' he replied dryly. Then, his voice quickening with concern, he added, 'Sara, you're not going to faint, are you?'

'I'm trying not to,' she quavered. 'Do you think I could have a drink of water? I think I'll be all right then.'

Janos put an arm about her shoulders, but his touch was quite impersonal as he supported her as she had once supported him. He guided her into the kitchen and pushed her down on to a chair. The sickness which was so unusual for her and which had been bothering her for a week or so was fast going away, leaving her with an unpleasant taste in her mouth and a strange desire to lie down and sleep.

'Here's the water.' Janos stood before her holding out a glass. She took it from him, drank half the water and looked around the kitchen, grimacing at the peeling walls, the broken cupboards and dirty floor.

'This place is a mess,' she said.

'I agree. But one day it will be cleared up.'

'How can you live here when it's like this?'

'I'm not living here. I come every day and try to do some job or other, but at night I stay at the Pheasant Inn. I have rented a room there. Are you all right now?'

Sara looked up. Arms folded across his chest, Janos was watching her with narrowed eyes.

'Yes, thank you.'

He held out his gloved hand for the glass and she gave it to him.

'Will you . . . will you ever be able to play the violin again the way you used to play it?' she whispered, forcing the words out.

'Time will tell,' he replied coldly. 'Is there anything else you want to know or see?'

Ida had been right, Sara thought. His pride was a high wall which was hard to climb. There was no forgiveness in him this time, no softening towards her, and it had been a mistake for her to come.

'No, not really,' she replied, rising to her feet. 'I'll go now.'

She unlatched the back door and stepped outside, then turned as she remembered something. Janos was just behind her, having followed her to the door and the rays of the westering sun lit up his face, revealing lines of pain and suffering graven into the cheeks and across the forehead. But his eyes were cold and blank, looking at her but not seeing her, dismissing her as someone he didn't care for.

'There is something else?' he queried politely.

'Yes. I ... I've filed for a divorce. Did you hear from the lawyer?'

'I did.'

'You ... you haven't replied.'

'No, but I will, given time. You will excuse me now, please. I would like to go and clear up the paint that spilled.'

He stepped back into the house and the door swung shut. For a few seconds Sara stood and stared at the scarred paintwork of the door. She should feel angry at the way he had treated her, but she didn't. She felt defeated because he had behaved differently from the way she had expected him to behave; because he hadn't tried to seduce her with words of love; because he had been cool and offhand.

Slowly she walked round the house to the front and got into her car. Where should she go now? To Stonethwaite? Staring through the windscreen at the sun-gilded rough greyish-brown bark of the old elm tree under which the car was parked, she acknowledged ruefully to herself that she had never intended to go to Stonethwaite when she had set out that afternoon. It had been only an excuse to drive this way; an excuse with which she had deluded herself. She had set out to see Janos because she had wanted to see him and had hoped he would ask her to stay with him. Above all she had hoped he would have asked her to give up all thoughts of a divorce and withdraw her petition for one.

But he hadn't, and now she didn't know what

to do. Almost automatically she started the car and drove it down the driveway to the road. Turning right she drove up the hill towards the Pheasant Inn. There were several cars parked outside and she guessed it must be full of guests at this time of the year. There would be no room for her at the inn, except . . .

The idea which flashed into her mind surprised her because it was so unlike anything she had ever considered doing in her life. It was so bold and so—well, yes, she had to face it—so utterly feminine, the sort of behaviour she looked down upon in other women. Something Cecilia would have had no hesitation in doing.

Yet perhaps it was the only way in which she was going to breach the wall of Janos's pride, the only way she was going to get near enough to him to be able to admit she had made a mistake. But could she do it? Could she seduce him?

Right into Kendal she drove, and was on her way out of the old grey town when she came to a decision. Stopping the car, she reversed into a convenient driveway and drove back towards the town parking by the river. From there she walked back to Finkle Street and into a shop that sold women's clothing.

The lingerie which the shop stocked was not exactly of the exotic variety, but there was one nightdress which appealed to her. Made from sheer black nylon with a ruffled neckline and long full sleeves caught at the wrist with more ruffles, it hinted seductively at all that it purported to conceal. Sara bought it and returned to the car, and soon she was driving along the road to the Pheasant Inn again.

There were changes in the inn. It had been enlarged and now possessed a proper dining room as well as a comfortable lounge cluttered cosily with antiques, brass, fresh flowers and many books. Sara found George Kent in the bar preparing for the evening invasion of customers. He remembered her at once.

'Come to join your hubby at last, have ye?' he said. 'Maggie and I have been wondering when you would.'

'Is he here?' Sara asked cautiously.

'No, he's down at yon house. Won't be back until the daylight's gone.'

'I wonder if I could go up to his room, to leave my things there. I'll be staying the night, if that's all right with you.'

'Aye, it'll be right,' he said. 'Will ye be wanting any dinner? I have to ask ye because we're pretty full tonight. We get a lot of non-resident diners now. Maggie's oxtail soup and home-made pies are popular.'

'Er . . . well, I'd prefer not to dine in the dining room, but I would like something to eat. I . . . I'm feeling very tired and I'd like to go to bed early.'

'The best thing you can do,' said George, lowering his voice, 'is to go and see Maggie. I know she'll be glad to see you. Proper worried she's been about yon hubby of yours, she has.

Says it isn't right for him to be here and you to be down there in Manchester. She's a bit old-fashioned like, is Maggie. Doesn't hold with those modern marriages.'

As soon as Sara walked into the kitchen where Maggie was supervising two other women who were helping her to prepare the food which would be served at dinner, the innkeeper's wife's face lit up.

'Ee, lass I'm right glad to see ye,' she said. 'Have ye come to stay?'

'For tonight anyway,' said Sara. 'I'd like to go to my husband's room, if that's possible. I'm feeling a bit tired.'

'Aye, ye do look pale. Come on then, I'll take you over to it. Since we've become busier we've turned the loft over the stable into a spare bedroom and Mr Cranston has been sleeping there. It means he can come and go without using the inn. Does he know you've come?'

'Er . . . he doesn't know I've come to stay,' said Sara evasively as they entered the lower part of the stable and started up the wooden stairway leading to the loft. 'And I'd be glad if you didn't say anything to him when he returns from the house by the lake. I want to surprise him.'

'I won't say anything,' said Maggie with a knowing little chuckle. 'I don't suppose I'll see him anyway.'

She pushed open the wooden door at the top of the stairs and they went into the room under the steep roof.

'Ye'll see George has made a good job of it,' she said proudly. 'Insulated the walls and the roof, made it real cosy like. He's even installed a bathroom up here. Now what about something to eat? Are you going to have dinner?'

'No . . . I'd rather not eat in the dining room,' said Sara, looking round the room. As Maggie had said, it was cosy, decorated in warm chintzy colours and it was furnished with a double bed, plain chests of drawers and two armchairs and a small table.

'Then when you're ready come down to the kitchen and have a bite to eat there.' Maggie's shrewd grey eyes were assessing as their glance flicked over Sara's face and figure. 'You're a lot thinner than I remember ye. Been working too hard, I expect. You ought to give it up settle down at home and look after yon man of yours. He needs looking after, mark my words.' She moved towards the door. 'Make yourself at home now, and come to the kitchen any time.'

Two hours later, having eaten in the kitchen, Sara returned to the room above the old stable loft. The long northern twilight was beginning to fade into night as darkness crept slowly across the sky from the east, but Janos had not yet returned from the house by the lake. After bathing in the small bathroom Sara dressed in the new black nightgown and wished she had a long mirror in which to survey herself. All she could see in the old-fashioned Victorian mirror on one of the chest of drawers were her head and shoulders. The translucent black material of the gown certainly accentuated the whiteness of her skin, she thought, and it enhanced the coppery lights in her hair. But her face looked greyish and her eyes lacked sparkle.

Cool and clear as the sea until you smile, then they sparkle with sunshine. You should smile more often. You are very pretty when you do.

Janos's words, spoken that morning when she had invited him to go with her to Stonethwaite, came back to mock her, and her lips quivered and her eyes filled with tears. She didn't look pretty now. She looked drawn and miserable and her mouth drooped discontentedly at the corners. How could she possibly hope to entice him to make love to her when she looked like this? Making a great effort, she tried to smile at her reflection, but all she produced was a grimace, and with a groan of disgust at herself she turned away from the mirror and picking up the book she had borrowed from the lounge she climbed into the bed and after arranging the pillows in a heap behind her she settled down to read.

Half an hour later she caught herself nodding over the book. Jerking her head back and opening her heavy eyes she picked up her watch from the bedside table. Half-past nine and outside it was almost completely dark. Stars twinkled at her through the window across which she had forgotten to draw the chintz curtains. Surely Janos would be here soon. Even if he had decided to eat at the inn he would have come here first to wash and change his clothes.

Mr Cranston. Sara's mouth twitched with humour, as she closed the book and leaned back against the pillows. He really was a mischievous devil, not using his own name but hers, not letting on to the Kents that he was the celebrated violinist Vaszary, 'the leader of the new generation of violinists', as one critic had described him, 'the brightest star in a new galaxy.'

And what would the critics or the adoring public which attended his concerts or bought his records think if they knew what he was doing now? If they knew he was hiding away in a dale among the fells of the English Lake District, renovating an old house? They wouldn't believe it. Either that or they would be offended because he had decided not to entertain them any more.

Feeling her eyes droop again, Sara turned and switched off the light. Staring out at the stars, forcing her eyes to stay open, she wondered why she had been feeling so tired lately. It couldn't be only lovesickness for Janos, surely. It must be something else, some virus she had picked up perhaps because she had become run down with not sleeping enough? What was that complaint she had heard about which produced the symptoms of perpetual tiredness and lack of vitality? Whatever was it called? Her eyelids drooped again and suddenly she was whirling down and down into the feather-bed softness of sleep.

She was at the concert again in California, sitting beside Glenn Bixman. She could feel the bulk of his shoulders against hers. Her eyes were closed and she was listening to a high sweet melody played on the violin; a haunting, tantalisingly romantic melody, the first she had ever heard Janos play.

She opened her eyes quickly fully expecting to find herself in the auditorium on the university campus in California, sitting with other people and looking up at a tall elegantly dressed man on a brightly lit stage. Instead she saw misty sunlight coming through a dormer window. Against the light was silhouetted the head and broad bare shoulders of a man who was playing the violin.

Sara blinked, thinking it was all part of the dream she had been having, expecting the music to fade away and darkness to come back. But the music went on erupting in a series of rushed cheerful chords and the room stayed light. It was morning and Janos was really there playing the violin. She heaved herself up in the bed looking round. The pillow next to hers was crumpled and dented, the bedclothes were tossed over on to her. Looking down, she became aware of the black nightdress and fingered it. What had happened last night? She couldn't remember.

'Oh, what happened? What happened?' she cried, clutching her head in her hands. 'Please tell me what happened?'

Janos stopped playing, dragging his bow across the strings. Lowering the violin, he turned to look at her. Since he had his back to the light now it was difficult to see the expression on his face.

'What happened when?' he asked coolly, laying down the violin and bow on the small table and coming across to the bed. Sweat gleamed on his shoulders and on his face, hinting that he had been playing energetically, and his hair was in a wild tangle. As he came near to her he thrust his scarred hands into his trouser pockets. He looked down at her curiously, his glance shifting over the black nightgown.

'Last night,' she whispered. Surely if they had made love she would have remembered. She would have felt differently anyway. She wouldn't have felt like this, all stiff and frozen, and, surprisingly, very shy.

'I'm not sure I know what you are talking about,' Janos replied. 'When I came to bed you were here, fast asleep. You were sleeping deeply and I did not like to waken you to ask you why you were here. So I will ask you now. Why are you here in my bed, Sara, dressed up in that nightgown?' A mocking smile tilted the corner of his lips and he sat down on the edge of the bed close to her.

Sara shrank back against the bedboard. In the darkness of the night she might have been able to do it, to reach out and touch him with passion. But daylight had the effect of freezing her up and it would take the touch of his passion to release her from the ice.

'I . . . I . . . was hoping we'd be able to talk if . . . if . . . I waited for you here,' she muttered, avoiding his glance. 'But you were such a long time coming.'

'If I had known you would be waiting here for me I would have come sooner,' Janos said softly, leaning towards her, and she looked up, sharply suspicious. Immediately he drew back, his mouth hardening, his eyes cold and hostile. 'You don't believe me, do you?' he accused harshly. 'You never have believed me. *God*, why do I bother to try and . . .'

Breaking off, he stood up suddenly, turning away to open a drawer in the chest, noisy violence in every action he made. He took out a clean shirt, slammed the door shut. Biting her lower lip and wondering what she should do next, Sara watched him thrust his arm into the sleeve of the shirt. It looked as if he might rip the material at any moment.

Then somehow she was off the bed and was standing in front of him, tall and slim, the whiteness of her limbs and breasts shining provocatively through the sheer nylon, her hair glowing in the sunshine which poured in through the window behind her.

The expression on Janos's face was enough to deter anyone from approaching him, and in the past she wouldn't have dared to speak to him when he had looked so fierce, black eyebrows lowering over eyes that blazed with a wicked yellow fire, his mouth curling in a sort of snarl back from his teeth. But the show of anger was preferable to the cold indifference with which he had treated her yesterday. It meant that he wasn't numb as Ida had suggested. It meant that he was still the hot-blooded, exuberant man she had married, her passionate stranger.

'I do believe you, Janos. I believe you now, she whispered frantically. 'I didn't believe you . . . for a while.'

'Or trust me,' he grated between taut lips as he began to fasten the buttons of his shirt.

'Or . . . or trust you,' she admitted.

'Or love me.'

'No, that isn't true. I did love you at first, but I . . . I . . . couldn't believe you loved me the way I wanted you to love me. I didn't come first with you. I was second fiddle to your music and career and so, and so . . .' Oh, God, she was making the same mistake. He was turning away from her. Stepping closer to him, Sara raised a hand to both of his which were busy with the next to top button of his shirt and she touched the back of one of them gently, stroking the scars as if her touch would make them disappear miraculously. 'You still have magic in your fingers,' she murmured, leaning against him until her hips and thighs were moving incitingly against his and the tips of her breasts were close to his hands. 'I could hear that magic in your playing just now. I wish I could *feel* that magic again. Touch me, Janos, let me feel it again.'

Her voice died away shyly and she bent her head to hide her suddenly burning cheeks. Fiddling with the buttons of his shirt, she undid them and when his chest was bare laid her cheek against its rough pulsing warmth, luxuriating in the feel of him, sniffing the musky male smell of him, savouring the taste of his skin with her tongue.

For a few frightening moments Janos held out, stiffening against her and she braced herself for rejection. Then, letting his breath out in a gusty sigh which was almost a groan of desire, he put his arms around her and rocked her gently as he might have rocked a child who had come to him for comfort. But the gentleness didn't last for long. His hands slid down her back to grip her buttocks and he ground her hips against his. Feeling the heat of his passion strike through her, Sara tipped back her head, her lips parting in invitation, her lashes drooping over his eyes. She had a brief glimpse of his face, distorted this time not with anger but desire, and then his lips were writhing against hers.

The bed came up beneath them suddenly, twanging as they fell across it. The nylon nightgown tore with a hiss, but Sara didn't regret its destruction. All that mattered now was to convince him that she loved him and wanted him. Sunlight, the sounds of birds singing, receded from her consciousness as she soared with Janos to their own private world of love, far above earthly problems and pain.

It was swift and complete, their union, a brief delirious high from which she floated down to become aware of the tangled bed, the heat of Janos's body, the sunshine gilding his skin, the throb of her own bruised lips and the wonderful delicious languor of her limbs.

'Does this coming to me of your own accord mean you are trusting me again?' Janos whispered, his lips hot against the curve of her throat, his hand sliding up over the flatness of her waist to the curve of her breast as he sought to rouse her again.

'Yes, oh, yes!' she breathed, turning to him, and suddenly, as if a dam had been breached by their physical union, words poured out of her and she admitted her mistake, explaining to him why she had been distrustful.

'If only you'd told me that you'd been accepted as an immigrant, shown me your papers,' she groaned. 'I would never have believed what Tom and Davina said about you. But you didn't.'

'I had told you once that my papers were all in order,' he replied. 'Yet still you doubted me, and my pride was hurt, knowing you believed them more than you believed me.'

'And you never denied that you'd made an arrangement to marry Cecilia . . .'

'Because I couldn't. Because I had made an arrangement with her, one I intended to get out of once I had met her again . . .'

'By pretending you'd fallen in love with me . . .'

'Ah, but you are wrong there, and if you had listened and heard me properly you would remember now that I told you I had fallen in love with you long before I knew about Cecilia's marriage to Philip. I fell in love with you the day I woke up at your flat and saw you bending over me. I fell in love with you in spite of the fact that you intended to deceive me and not take me to see Cecilia. And now I am falling in love with you for the third time.'

'Oh. When was the second time?'

'In California, when I saw you sitting in the audience.'

'You could really see me?'

'Not in detail, but Cecilia had told me where you would be sitting and I played for you, my love, especially the Sérénade. It was my serenade for Sara. And I came to you, at Cecilia's house, hoping to make you love me again, but you were not listening to me or trusting me—you were too taken up with your new admirer. So I had to leave you again.'

'Supposing—supposing I hadn't come to see you again yesterday, would you really have sent me an invitation to come and visit you here?' she asked.

'Perhaps,' Janos replied tormentingly. 'But why suppose? You came, and now our separation is over and nothing is ever going to come between us again, unless you are going to insist on going back to your job in Manchester today.'

'I don't have a job in Manchester any more,' she said, and was pushed away from him so he could look at her face.

'Why not?' he demanded.

'I resigned yesterday. Suddenly it was not important any more.'

'So what are you going to do now?'

'I'm going to stay with you and help you with the house. I'm going to clean and paint.'

'But not all the time, Sara. Sometimes we'll take time off and walk in the woods, climb the hills,' he whispered, 'explore together and make love together.'

'Yes, we'll take time off,' she agreed happily. 'But I'm going to nag and nag and nag at you to practise the violin until you can play again like an angel. And then when your hands are completely healed I'm going with you on your next concert tour. I'm tired of being left behind when you go away. I'm free now, at last, free to do what I want and go where I wish and I want to be with you, go where you go ...' She broke off, suddenly unsure of herself again, and hid her face against his throat. 'That is ... if it's what you want,' she mumbled.

'It is what I want more than anything else in the world,' Janos surprised her by saying, and Sara raised her head to look at him again.

'You ... you're sure?'

'I'm sure. You see, since I damaged my hands I have had plenty of time to think ... about you mostly ... but also about me, and I have discovered that though performing music in public is still very necessary to me it isn't more important to me than you are. It doesn't come first with me any more. You do.' Janos drew her against him, his hands sliding caressingly again. 'I love you,

Sara, very much, and I would like us to start our marriage all over again and build a life together, not apart. There will be children too, I hope.'

'I hope so too,' she said fervently, realising that the wounds inflicted on him by the death of Eva and their child had healed at last. And as their lips met tenderly in a prelude to the slow exquisite rousing of their desire for each other she wondered with a little tingle of excitement if that strange sickness which she had been experiencing lately meant that she was pregnant, having conceived when they had met in California.

But there would be plenty of time to tell Janos about it later. All the time in the world, now that they were together again.

Harlequin Plus

A WORD ABOUT THE AUTHOR

Ever since she can remember, Flora Kidd has cherished a longing to sail the seas—not on a big ocean liner, but in a sailboat. This great love brought her into contact with her husband-to-be, Wilf, who shared her dream. And over the years, they and their four children have sailed the waters of the Old World and the New (today they make their home in New Brunswick, one of Canada's maritime provinces).

Flora's decision to write came about while she was living in a seaside village in the south of Scotland. Looking for something to read, she borrowed several romance novels and afterward remarked to a friend, "I think I could write a story like these." To which the friend replied, "Maybe you could, but would anyone want to read it?"

That was the necessary challenge! Flora's first Romance, *Nurse at Rowanbank* (#1058), was published in 1966 and her first Presents, *Dangerous Pretence* (#212), appeared in 1977. She is now a best-selling author of more than twenty Romances and fifteen Presents.

Take these 4 best-selling novels FREE

 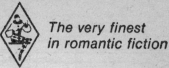

Harlequin Presents...

The very finest in romantic fiction

Get all the latest books before they're sold out!

As a Harlequin subscriber you actually receive your personal copies of the latest Presents novels immediately after they come off the press, so you're sure of getting all 6 each month.

Cancel your subscription whenever you wish!

You don't have to buy any minimum number of books. Whenever you decide to stop your subscription just let us know and we'll cancel all further shipments.

Your FREE gift includes

Sweet Revenge by **Anne Mather**
Devil in a Silver Room by **Violet Winspear**
Gates of Steel by **Anne Hampson**
No Quarter Asked by **Janet Dailey**

FREE Gift Certificate
and subscription reservation

Mail this coupon today!

In the U.S.A.
1440 South Priest Drive
Tempe, AZ 85281

In Canada
649 Ontario Street
Stratford, Ontario N5A 6W2

Harlequin Reader Service:

Please send me my 4 Harlequin Presents books free. Also, reserve a subscription to the 6 new Harlequin Presents novels published each month. Each month I will receive 6 new Presents novels at the low price of $1.75 each [*Total – $10.50 a month*]. There are no shipping and handling or any other hidden charges. I am free to cancel at any time, but even if I do, these first 4 books are still mine to keep absolutely FREE without any obligation.

_____
NAME   (PLEASE PRINT)

_____
ADDRESS

_____
CITY   STATE / PROV.   ZIP / POSTAL CODE

Offer expires May 31, 1982
Offer not valid to present subscribers   BP464

Prices subject to change without notice.